D0069777

A Caregiver's Handbook to Perinatal Loss

Gary E. Vogel, M.A., N.C.C.
Licensed Mental Health Counselor
Nationally Certified Counselor
Winter Park, Florida

A Place To Remember
A subsidiary of deRuyter-Nelson Publications, Inc.
Saint Paul, Minnesota

Copyright © 1996
deRuyter-Nelson Publications, Inc.

Cover Design by Bob Wasiluk

All Rights Reserved

Publication Data
Vogel, Gary E.
A Caregiver's Guide to Perinatal Loss / Gary E. Vogel,
p. cm.
Includes biographical references
ISBN 0-9650848-0-9 (trade paper)
1. Perinatal death - Psychological aspects
2. Perinatal death - Caregivers
3. Bereavement - Psychological aspects
4. Grief - Caregivers
5. Grief Therapy

Printed in the United States of America

deRuyter-Nelson Publications, Inc.
1885 University Avenue, Suite 110
Saint Paul, Minnesota 55104

Dedicated to Chelsea Francis Evelyn Vogel
November 26, 1989
Forever our baby

Table of Contents

Preface

I hope that as you read this book it's clear that I have spent several years researching these issues. I have years of psycho-therapeutic experience and have interviewed countless grieving parents and professional caregivers in order to obtain a broad overview of the intricacies of perinatal loss. At the same time, you should know that this book was written not only from professional research and evaluation, but also from the personal experience after the trauma of the full-term stillbirth of my daughter, Chelsea.

After the stillbirth, my wife, Kathy, stayed home for six weeks to recover from delivering a full-term baby. I went back to work. I came home in between appointments when I could, but I was mostly back to my usual routine.

Kathy cried a lot. Some of her cries I understood. The others, I struggled with. I still cried, but only occasionally.

Soon the cards stopped coming. The calls slowed to a trickle, and no one was stopping by. Then it was just us.

People began using me as a source of information. "What can we do?" "How's Kathy doing?" I answered the questions and became the insulation between Kathy and the world. In my male role of provider and fixer, I was doing what I thought I was supposed to do—I was taking care of my family.

But it wasn't working. Kathy was still crying. I suggested a vacation, thinking that if we got away from the pain, we'd be "better."

We had a wonderful week of seashore, snow, and mountains in North Carolina. We talked endlessly. We even made love for the first time since our life was turned upside down. She didn't cry as much. We even laughed. I felt we were back on track. I had fixed it! I had finally been successful at finding the right combination of actions to take care of my family.

I was shocked when upon our return Kathy mentioned going to a support group. I thought we were doing OK. Again though, trying to be supportive, I agreed.

Over the next seven weeks I learned that despite all my professional training, I had taken the typically male approach to pregnancy loss. Kathy resented my life being normal again. She resented that we were not grieving together and the distance that created between us.

We both came to understand that our loss was different. I came to understand that she felt biological failure even if I didn't.

We came to understand that we had very different styles of grieving. She was more emotional, I was more intellectual. Our styles worked for each of us, but not when imposed on the other.

With this increased understanding of each other came an increased feeling of safety. We felt safe to express our perceptions to the other. Neither would criticize, but we'd listen and offer our different perspectives. When we respected each other's grieving styles, our initial closeness returned.

You would think that as a trained psychotherapist I would know all these things. My experience is just another example of how we can lose our objectivity when it's our own life—when the pain is our own. All my training and experience went flying out the window and I fell into a very typical male role.

Since then we have given birth to a premature, but healthy son, Geoffrey. After he was born, I agreed to facilitate a support group for couples who had experienced pregnancy and infant loss. Now I speak regularly on the subject and do a great deal of in-service training for nurses, clergy and therapists. I have written extensively on the issues of pregnancy loss, and it has become a large part of my professional life.

I am often asked: "Isn't it hard to do this work?" My answer is always the same: "Not at all. All that I do now is my way of giving meaning to such a short life, just as Chelsea has given new meaning to mine. It's my way of answering the 'Why?' question."

Forward

This book was written for the professional caregiver. Extraneous detail has been eliminated since I assume a professional is likely to have a basic understanding of grief issues and normal professional-to-client skills. I point out issues, discuss them briefly, and where appropriate, give suggested interventions. Remember that while some of these issues can be complex because of their uniqueness to perinatal loss, most are pretty straightforward.

My purpose is to give you a concise explanation of issues related specifically to perinatal loss. My intention is not only to inform and update, but also to validate and verify what you may already know. This book will more likely re-educate and reinforce rather than educate the totally uninformed.

Some caregivers "freeze up" and do nothing because they are afraid of possibly doing the wrong thing and harming the patient. This fear is usually based in ignorance or unfamiliarity, and I hope this book will provide enough comfort with the issues that this anxiety will be disarmed.

To these ends, *A Caregiver's Handbook to Perinatal Loss* is intended to be a reference text. It should not be read once and disposed of, but rather it should be read and referred to as needed. Because of the sheer volume of demands on the professional caregiver, my brevity was purposeful. I see a greater need for a book that can be read quickly rather than a book which expounds in excruciating detail each individual issue. There are several books (some of them are noted in the Bibliography) which might provide more comprehensive detail should the reader care to delve more deeply into specific issues related to perinatal loss.

Since there is a great deal of cross-over from one discipline to the next, I encourage you to read of all sections in this book, whether or not they address your specific discipline. For example, many issues that clergy face also confront funeral directors; or physicians may gain an added perspective by understanding the issues that more directly confront those in the nursing profession. Without doubt, reading each others' sections will be advantageous.

Familiarizing oneself with issues in all disciplines will also be helpful in another regard: as professionals, we often feel reluctant to admit to patients, "I don't know" for fear of appearing incompetent. But, if "I don't know" is followed by "but I'll find out and get back to you," an entirely different message is conveyed. I hope this book will provide a resource for much of what you might need to "find out."

You may find certain disciplines suspiciously absent, such as Nurse Midwives, Hospital Administrators (including Risk Management), and Emergency Medical Technicians. These disciplines, while valid in their own right, have very similar issues to other disciplines that are discussed. For example, a Certified Nurse Midwife with whom I consulted felt that a section devoted exclusively to her profession would be redundant. Her field is basically a combination of both nursing and obstetrics, two areas already addressed. Both a Hospital Administrator and an EMT I consulted had similar feedback. This reinforces the argument that you should read the entire book regardless of your discipline.

Although I do not presume to recommend against the lay public reading this book, it is, however, geared more for those whose grasp of the situation is based upon their professional experience. This book was not designed to assist the bereaved in their own healing process.

A professional recommending this book to those who have incurred loss needs to guage the patients' perceived ability to incorporate emotionally objective information into their individual grieving process. After all, patients need to understand the grieving process on *all* of its levels. So before you recommend this book, remember that there are many excellent books written specifically for the bereaved which will approach these issues on a much more affective, rather than intellectual, level.

Perinatal Loss Issues

What we call the beginning
is often the end
and to make our ends
is to make a beginning
the end is where we start from
— T. S. Eliot

As helping professionals, we have all come in contact with someone who has a profound impact on our professional lives. Sometimes this person may be someone we didn't know very long, but nevertheless is someone we will never forget. Perinatal loss creates an intense situation in which just such a profound impact can be made. This everlasting impression also works in reverse, and part of the job of the caregiver is to make the impression on the bereaved a positive one.

Perinatal loss also creates a situation in which the mother will be greatly impacted by the brief relationship she has had with her baby. The death of someone who is valuable to us is always traumatic, but as is so often the case, we don't realize *how* important that person was to us until after they died. This cannot be more intensely exemplified than in the death of a child who has yet to experience their own birth.

When a mother learns she is pregnant, she instantly perceives that she is now a mother. She is carrying, and caring for, her child—not a number of cells that will eventually become a child, but a child. At that moment, she and her partner begin adjusting to the new reality of parenthood. Almost immediately they begin to look at life itself from a different perspective. They are filled with the expectation of a future with that child, and the unselfishness that accompanies being responsible for a child's life.

And then, sometime with little or no warning, just as quickly as it began, it's over. In an instant, the hopes, dreams and expectations of the future are gone. The young life that the parents have become so emotionally invested in, is over.

Now, where there was once ecstatic joy, there is only excruciating pain. And worse yet, all that is often left as a reminder of the life that was once there, is the pain.

Some of what has been lost is concrete, some of it is abstract. But the feeling of loss is overwhelming for those who have experienced perinatal loss. This is partly because the sense of loss is so pervasive that it encompasses all aspects of life. It is also partly due to the abstract nature of the loss which causes some parents to feel so confused, that they perceive their own emotions are betraying them.

The Loss

When a child dies through perinatal loss, grief is overwhelming because the sense of loss is overwhelming. Many people are confused about the association between grief, death, and loss. We don't actually grieve death, we grieve the loss of the person as a part of our life. Death is the vehicle that took them away from us; death caused the loss.

When an elder dies, we grieve the loss of that part of our life we shared with them. We won't be able to share that part of us with them anymore. However, we have memories of times shared, fondness recalled, and hopefully, tangible items from the person to attach our feelings to. These tangible mementos become extremely important, for they now represent the person we've lost.

Even though our sense of loss is great when an elder dies, their death was in the natural order of things. Death is something that is "supposed" to happen at the end of a long and fulfilled life, and as a result our acceptance of their passing comes relatively easily.

A perinatal loss presents a unique sense of loss. We still grieve the loss of that part of our life we shared with them, but on many levels it is different. The mother shared with her child a part of her life emotionally, and also physically. This is a unique sense of "connectedness" that the father, as a man, will probably not begin to understand.

Unlike other kinds of loss through death, in perinatal loss the loss of what parents *have shared* with their child in the past is probably not as intense as the loss of what they will now *not be able to share* with their child. Their loss of the future is probably more strongly felt than their loss of the past.

Depending on when the loss occurs, the loss of this future may be abstract or concrete. The deciding factor that determines the concreteness of the loss is the level of bonding that has taken place. Even in an early miscarriage, if the mother has bonded very strongly with her baby, her sense of loss will be very real. However, the obverse is also true: if attachment has not yet taken place, no matter when in the course of the pregnancy, the loss is more abstract.

The loss of the future that was being planned with the baby is only one part of the sense of loss.

Also lost is the opportunity to give and receive love unconditionally, as uniquely experienced between parent and child.

Another loss is that of identity. Personal roles such as "I'm Jessica's father" or "Kyle's mother" will not be a role that will be played out with this child. A sense of identity that goes along with continuing family lineage and the parents role in the family tree is also lost.

In our culture, as in many throughout the world, having a child is a rite of passage. Once a person has a child, they are no longer a child themselves. They are truly accepted into the ranks of adulthood. If the perinatal loss is a first child, this, then, can represent the loss of acceptance into adulthood.

One of the more abstract losses is the loss of the feeling of being in control of one's own life. Most people grow up thinking that they are in control of their own destiny. Pregnancy, usually a situation that was carefully monitored and deferred to, is usually thought of as a situation that is in our control. This is especially true for the mother who is physically connected with, and therefore has so much influence over, the child within her. The fact that the mother had so much impact and influence over her child and could do nothing to prevent the child's death, makes it glaringly clear how little we are in control over life. If we can't ensure a positive outcome in this situation, then what can we control?

Since most child bearing couples tend to be younger, this loss of control over destiny is a great loss. The acceptance of this reality is at the very core of our own mortality. Most younger parents are unprepared to face this reality at this stage in life, and especially unprepared to be forced to face it under these difficult circumstances.

Conversely, in today's world, for a variety of reasons, couples are often making the decision to delay childbearing until later in life. These couples are often facing a diminishing window of opportunity for having a child. As these couples face perinatal loss, the possibility of being childless becomes startlingly real. Also, since later pregnancies tend to be more planned, the loss of the sense of control over their lives can be even greater than with younger couples.

Another reality is the increasing numbers of mothers who choose to have children as single parents. For them, the loss of the opportunity to give and receive unconditional love can be an extremely significant loss.

A recognition of the myriad of possible losses, in addition to the obvious loss of the baby, is essential for the caregiver. The reason for this is simple—as a caregiver, your role is to provide for the needs of your patient. With this loss, one of the greatest needs of the bereaved is validation. Validation is a term that is often used in this book, and it deserves definition.

In this circumstance, validation can best be described as letting the patient know that their grief is legitimate because their loss is a valid loss. The best method of legitimizing their loss is to be able to identify and share with them all of their losses, both concrete and abstract. Only then will they begin to understand their feelings—an essential step in their ability to progress through their grief.

Grief

As was stated before, the need to grieve is directly related to the importance of what we have lost. To a parent, nothing is more important than their child. There is not a more catastrophic loss than the loss of their child. Consequently, the need to thoroughly grieve this loss is extremely important.

However, our society is still sending mixed messages about the need to grieve a perinatal loss. In fact, the legitimacy of the need to grieve this loss has only recently been recognized. Even the mental health community has only recently accepted that the loss of pregnancy is a staggering and significant loss.

In the Third (revised) Edition of the *Diagnostic and Statistical Manual of Mental Disorders* (DSM), published in 1987, there existed a "Severity of Psychosocial Stressors Scale." This scale was created to rate the severity and impact of certain acute and chronic events. On this scale, miscarriage was considered to be only moderately stressful, but the death of a child was rated catastrophic. As recently as 1987, it was not understood, even within the mental health community, that the psychological impact on a parent from a miscarriage or from the loss of a child could be the same.

The publication of *Disenfranchised Grief* by Kenneth J. Doka in 1989 was a major leap in understanding grief that was deemed inappropriate by another's standard of measurement. His work was based upon the premise that grief tends to be "disenfranchised" when the loss associated with the grief is not recognized by society as significant. Outwardly portraying grief in any way is considered inappropriate and illegitimate. Perinatal death is discussed at length in his work as an example of a loss that our society still does not fully recognize as valid or legitimate.

With the publication of *Diagnostic and Statistical Manual of Mental Disorders IV* in 1994, the "Severity of Psychosocial Stressors Scale" was replaced by simply stating the "Psychosocial or Environmental Problem." This eliminated the need to rate the legitimacy of the loss, and made for a much more unilateral understanding that the need to grieve was individual, not necessarily societal.

It is, therefore, the job of a caregiver to validate the parent's grief to the level of the parent's need, not the caregiver's. Understand that there are no rules for grieving, only guidelines. Grief is an individual experience and needs to be ratified as such.

In order to better understand what grief is, it is often helpful to understand what grief is not. Below is a list of common myths concerning grief. These myths address most patients' misconceptions and fears about grief.

Common Myths About Grief

Myth 1: Grief is a feeling.
Grief is actually a process composed of many feelings.

Myth 2: Grief and mourning are the same experience.
Grief is the thought and feeling experienced within oneself upon the death of someone loved. Grief is the internal meaning given to the experience of bereavement. Mourning is taking the internal experience of grief and expressing it outside of oneself. The specific ways in which people express mourning are influenced by many things: customs of their culture, gender, and nature of the loss.

Myth 3: The experience of mourning is predictable and orderly.
Even though there are certain identifiable stages of the grieving experience, people mourn in different ways. Expecting anything less would be to demonstrate a lack of respect for the uniqueness of the person.

Myth 4: Moving away from grief is preferable to moving towards it.

People who continue to express their grief outwardly are often viewed as weak, crazy, or self-pitying. Often they are told to "shape up and get on with life." Many people view grief as a difficulty to overcome rather than experience. Unfortunately, the result of these types of messages is to encourage the repression of the griever's thoughts and feelings, which lead to future complications.

Myth 5: The goal of grief is to get over it.

The pain from the loss changes from an ever-present, sharp, almost unbearable pain to an acknowledged feeling that the loss has given new meaning and purpose. The sense of loss doesn't completely disappear, but softens and becomes less acute. Hope emerges as the griever is able to make commitments to the moving on of their own life, with the knowledge that the person lost will not be forgotten.

Myth 6: Tears expressing grief are a sign of weakness.

Totally false. The capacity of the griever to share their tears is an indication of their willingness to do the work of mourning.

Stages of Grief

Grief does have certain predictable and identifiable stages that need to be understood. For ease of understanding, I find it less overwhelming to break it down to just three basic stages. Keep in mind that these stages of grief are not necessarily experienced in the order stated. And, just because someone has experienced a certain stage, it does not necessarily mean that they are done with that stage. They may need to re-experience it at a later stage in their grieving process. If that happens, they may need validation that they aren't doing grief wrong.

Avoiding the New Reality: The most predominant features of this stage in grief are shock and denial. Whenever we are confronted with something that is overwhelming, our first reaction is disbelief. Sometimes this will actually be verbalized in variations of "I can't believe this is happening!" Initial denial is our way of escaping from reality until we can adequately deal with the trauma. Often, we need time to break an overwhelming situation down into more workable pieces, and denial is one method we use to give ourselves that time.

Being in shock, on the other hand, is the numbness that is experienced when the trauma is occurring. It is this emotional detachment from the situation and the surroundings which can actually assist those going through trauma to do what they need to do at the time—it will allow the patient to be compliant and do what is necessary. Keep in mind, however, that everyone responds to shock differently, and some people may become non-compliant or even abusive.

When a couple incurs a perinatal loss, they will have the need to avoid the new reality for a time. Usually this will take place when the loss has just occurred, but they also may have the need to revisit denial later. Oddly enough, in a perinatal loss, revisiting denial can be a way of forcing remembrance. For example, in a pregnancy loss, a baby was anticipated, but never brought home. The house has no signs of the baby's presence; nothing physically has changed. As the parents walk through their home and *don't* feel the presence of the baby, they will be allowed to revisit denial. However, as they move from the denial stage, the realization of their denial may provide the very incentive to find mementos that will play a role in their remembrance process.

These temporary forms of denial, however, are totally different than the form experienced by someone who does not, and apparently will not, admit to others or themselves that the baby has died. Some will insist that the baby is still growing within them, and can even feel the baby moving. This is the sign of serious pathology that has been triggered by the loss, and a referral for psychiatric treatment needs to be made.

For most grieving parents, denial is a stage that they need to move through in order to begin the healing process. The vast majority will break through their denial when they are ready to begin accepting the loss as a part of their lives.

Admitting the New Reality: When grieving parents no longer need the protection afforded to them by denial, they will move into another stage in the grieving process—one characterized by a great deal of pain. While denial protected them from pain, it was an unrealistic state which couldn't continue. And although they may have the need to be without the pain for a short time, allowing them to revisit denial, they cannot remain there indefinitely. Healing requires pain. Growth requires pain.

The pain of loss comes in a variety of forms. Being depressed, for example, is a natural response when we have lost someone very valuable to us. Patients can express depression in a variety of ways. Some cry. Some get numb. Some turn their depression, usually expressed as anger, on themselves.

Anger is really another form of pain, and being angry is natural and normal. It can be difficult to express anger at a situation, so often the anger is taken out on a person close to them—usually someone with whom they feel safe. As a caregiver, having the anger directed at you is a compliment of sorts, but one that is difficult to decipher at the time. It's best not to personalize the anger. Remember that you, as a professional, are competent and capable. Responding to the patient: "If I we're in your shoes, I'd be angry too," is probably the most effective way to disarm the situation.

A spouse, however, who is having anger directed at them may carry their own anger at the situation, and may respond by returning anger back. This will create more distance between spouses at a time when they need each other the most. In addition, the spouse who originally vented anger may later feel guilty about forgetting that their partner is also hurting.

Patients may feel anger toward their God, which can can result in a feeling of extreme guilt. Many believe they're not supposed to be angry at God, to whom they feel they owe all. They need to understand that any supreme being would be supremely forgiving, even of their anger.

Guilt is another extremely painful emotion. Patients may feel guilty for having done something, or *not* done something, during the pregnancy. They may feel guilty for having smoked,having drank liquor, having sex, or exercising. The list is endless. Remember, whether or not the occurrences may be valid, the guilt is very real.

They will often feel guilty for what they didn't do. The father, especially, may feel guilty that he didn't uphold his male responsibility of protecting his family from harm. He may feel guilty for anything that may have had even a possible impact on his partner.

The mother may feel guilty for not upholding her responsibility for the life within her that was totally dependent on her. Her sense of failure will be overwhelming.

Usually these varying forms of guilt are expressed something like: "If only...", or "I should (or shouldn't) have...." They are attempting to second guess what they might have done to change the outcome. As is always the case, hindsight always seems to be clearer. The reality is that the patient did what they did because it seemed right at the time. Remember, however, that simply reminding them of that won't instantaneously make their guilt vanish. Guilt can be a way of doing penance, and they may need to do that for awhile.

Guilt can also occur later. For example, parents will often return to denial when they have the need to. They may then feel guilty when they interpret this denial as an attempt to forget their baby. In reality, they don't want to forget, they just need to be without the pain for a while. This often presents a dilemma. They need to be reassured that there is a difference between *forgetting* and *not thinking about.* Reassure them that they will *not* forget and that it *is* alright to not think about their baby all of the time.

Remember that guilt can also be an attempt to answer the "Why?" question. And whether it's, "Why did this happen?" or, "Why did this happen *to us*?", there can be no truly acceptable answer to the question. As a result, they will often turn the blame onto themselves.

No matter what the circumstances of the guilt are, keep in mind that guilt is a natural part of the grieving process.

Emptiness and loneliness are other ways in which the pain of the loss can be expressed. Post partum reactions to the emptiness of childbirth are common. Remember that the grieving mother does not have her arms full with her baby to compensate for her womb being empty. The ache of her loneliness speaks for itself.

During the early stages of grief, patients will feel many conflicting emotions, almost simultaneously. It is common that they may be trying to absorb so many aspects of the situation at the same time that they become confused. Emotional confusion is not being able to identify what it is that they're really feeling. Intellectual confusion is often expressed by forgetfulness, or by having difficulty completing tasks that were once considered basic. They may at times think they are "going crazy."

It will require patience on your part to help them understand that they are trying to intellectually and emotionally process so much information at once that their "circuits" are overloaded. Validating the patients' confusion (basically telling them, that for now, they *need* to be confused because it's part of the process) will probably be very repetitive and tiresome for you as the caregiver. However, keep in mind that a vital part of the validation process includes your reassurance that this confusion will pass.

Adapting to the New Reality: The parents will eventually reach the point when the acuteness of the pain will have subsided and they will feel they are beginning to return to their "normal" life. At the same time there is acceptance of the realization that they will never be the same. This is true. They are now different, and they have begun to accept their differences, even be grateful for them. They no longer want to return to "normal," meaning how they were before the loss. They now will look at life itself differently. Their priorities in life are different. Everything has changed for them, but now it's no longer just ugliness.

At this point they have begun the process of giving the death a meaningful place in their lives. They know they won't forget. They no longer want to. Incorporating the loss into their lives provides for them a depth and understanding of life that those who have not suffered and struggled with loss, will not yet have learned. They will have obtained that place of serenity where they have new meaning in their lives because of their baby. They have adapted their lives to embrace their loss. They will *become* the ultimate memorial.

Unfortunately, most caregivers will probably not get the privilege of witnessing this stage in the process. For most caregivers, they will need to be satisfied and cherish the knowledge that they contributed to the parents being able to get to this point. Always remember that each caregiver the parents have contact with along the way becomes the guide for that part of the journey.

Male vs. Female Grief

When a man and woman first come together as a couple, they bring to that relationship the personalities and characteristics which have been molded by their life experiences to that point. We accept, and sometimes enjoy, that we are partners despite our differences.

Suddenly with the loss of a baby, everything changes, including the relationship. Initially, couples may cling to one another in that moment of shock and disbelief. They may feel closer to one another than they have ever felt before. And, for this time, their grief feels identical.

But with the passage of time, the differences in grieving styles between men and women becomes more and more obvious. Each may feel emotionally isolated from the other at the very time they need each other the most.

Women are often more verbally expressive about their loss. They are more likely to seek support from others, and are often given comfort and support in their bereavement for a longer period of time. Men are more likely to grieve in cognitive and solitary ways. They usually disclose far less intimate information to others, and therefore tend to grieve privately.

Men tend to be action-oriented and "take control" of the loss experience. They are more likely to use anger as the expression for an entire range of emotions connected to the loss. Women, on the other hand, will usually express, and sometimes even explore, each individual emotion. This expression/exploration can be overwhelming for men in an already overwhelming situation.

Men tend to look at their roles as provider, problem-solver, and fixer. It is no different at the time of perinatal loss. Fathers will usually go back to work sooner than mothers. Of course, sometime the reason for this is physical, with the mother medically unable to return to work. But for whatever reason, the father is returning back to a so-called normal life much quicker than is the mother. She may resent this and may also feel abandoned by her partner by his return to work. Unfortunately, this may feel much like the abandonment she feels about her baby.

The role of problem-solver becomes increasingly difficult for fathers after perinatal loss. Men who see their partner in pain may think of the pain as a problem that needs solving. Often this means they will take any means available to try to make the pain go away. Taking trips, buying gifts, going out to dinner, or even just changing the subject all become ways to fix the pain. But often, the pain itself has become a memento of the baby for the mother, and she will feel a sense of betrayal to her baby without the pain. The mother's need to be with the pain for a time is normal. Unless fully understood, this male vs. female perception of the pain can cause a great deal of conflict in the relationship.

Previously, I discussed the difference between grief and mourning. For the most part, men grieve while women tend to mourn. Men will tend to keep their grief experience to themselves, while women will be more vocal in sharing their experience. But this difference can lead the grieving mother to believe that her partner doesn't care about the loss of the baby because "he's not showing it," while the grieving father will feel that his wife is an emotional wreck because she's always mourning. Both need to understand that while they are both grieving, they are doing it in their own ways.

There may be a vast difference in what feelings each is actually experiencing. For example, a mother will usually feel a sense of failure (guilt) that the father may not feel at all. To explain this, consider that, at the point of conception, the father's *biological* responsibility successfully ends. However, at the same moment, the mother's biological responsibility has just begun. She is now totally responsible for the child within her. When the baby dies, even though she may not be to blame, she still feels that responsibility. The father cannot relate to the mother's sense of failure.

This feeling of failure can often affect the mother's sense of self-esteem. She may feel that her body (and very femininity) have betrayed her. With self-image and self-esteem greatly impacted, a variety of effects, including depression, can occur. At the same time, the father's self-esteem is often relatively unaffected.

The bond that exists between a mother and her baby is unequaled in nature. Men simply cannot know what it is like to share their body with another being who is solely dependent on them. This difference once again puts distance between the partners when they need each other the most.

All caregivers need to be aware that some form of conflict will probably arise out of the differences in male vs. female grieving styles. Any caregiver who is in a position to do so (nurse, social worker, pastor, etc.), needs to tell the couple about the differences in grieving styles. For many couples, just addressing this reality will help them be more aware, and therefore better equipped, to cope with the differences when they happen.

In addition, any caregiver who sees destructive conflict between the couple and believes its origins to be rooted in differences between male vs. female grieving, needs to be prepared to confront this issue. After all, part of your role as caregiver is to extend to patients the care they *need, not* just the care you're comfortable giving them. Unfortunately, simply addressing the issue will probably not be enough. Once destructive conflict has been observed, it's probably significant enough to warrant the intervention of a trained therapist or referral to a support group equipped to manage this issue.

This referral needs to handled in a caring and compassionate manner, being careful not to give the label of victim or perpetrator to either parent. If, in your individual capacity, you do not feel prepared to address this issue with the parents, pass your observations on to someone more trained to do so.

Support Systems

Grandparents

Grandparents were anxiously awaiting the baby, too. They also lost a future they were so looking forward to. They grieve for the grandchild they will never watch grow up. At the same time, they grieve for their child who is probably in more pain than they have ever experienced before. As a parent, they will want to do anything they can think of to help .

Feeling helpless to make their child's pain go away, grandparents may sometimes get desperate. They may say or do things to try to make their child feel better, but often it backfires. Also keep in mind that the grandparents come from a different era in terms of dealing with perinatal loss, and may inadvertently offer hurtful advice.

Grandparents may need guidance as to how to best meet the current needs of their child. They may resent being told how to care for their child, but giving them guidelines may assist them to feel less helpless. They may just as likely respond better to suggestions from a caregiver whom they view as a professional. Be sure to affirm their experience with their child while redirecting their attention to the current needs of their child.

A significant way to accomplish this is to point out to the grandparents what they *can* do, and what they *can't* do. No matter how desperately they may want to, they can't take away their child's pain. Not even trying to is their best option. What they *can* do for their child is to be supportive (not overprotective), and to be willing to do what their child *needs* them to do. Stress that when they are in doubt as to what that might be, they need to ask rather than just do.

Family and Friends

All the different people around the grieving couple may react to the situation in very different ways. It would be wonderful if everyone was supportive and affirming during this difficult time, but the reality may be far different. The caregiver needs to prepare the couple for the varying reactions that they may receive from the people around them.

Parents need to understand that no one else had the relationship with the baby like they did. While they are struggling with their reality of the situation, others will struggle even more because they had no relationship at all with the baby. Many will try to minimize the parents' pain with phrases like: "At least...", or "It's for the best." Some will encourage them to get on with life and just have another baby.

The grieving couple needs to be prepared for these comments and know how to cope with them. A part of preparing them is to explain what is going on for most of these other people and what their comments mean. For the most part, these comments aren't meant to be hurtful, usually coming from well-meaning people who are trying to ease the pain of the loss. They truly don't have any idea that their comments are causing further difficulty. They are unaware that the couple doesn't *want* to "get over it," or replace their baby with another one.

Others will not feel the intensity of the loss as the parents do. They need to not be expected to. Some may say nothing and just stay away. This may heighten the feelings of abandonment that are already so pervasive in perinatal loss.

At the same time, just because family and friends may stay away, it doesn't necessarily mean they don't care. People often are afraid they will say or do something that will hurt the parents, so they make the decision to limit contact. Most often, these people are under the false assumption that talking about the baby heightens the parents' pain. Stress to the parents that family and friends may need to be assured that the pain already exists and that the parents *want* to have an opportunity to let some of it out by discussing it freely with the people that they feel safe with. With that understanding on the part of all parties, it becomes a compliment to any family member or friend that the parent feels so secure with them that they can express their most personal feelings.

The couple may have other friends who are pregnant. Many times, these friends will stay away. They may be either uncomfortable for themselves or for the griever. First of all, the griever needs to understand that this uncomfortableness may be the reason for the distance between them. Secondly, they will need to give their friends guidance as to what their needs are. It is the griever who needs to decide what is best for them. If it would help to be around a friend who is pregnant, for example, they need to discuss it with their friend. Be sure the friend is aware that while there will probably be tears, the griever is sad for themselves, while still being happy for their friend.

Prepare the couple for the fact that no one else knows their needs better than they do. They need to trust their own feelings, and what those feelings are telling them. Even if someone else has had a similar experience, they can't know what *they* are feeling. Others may feel helpless, and the griever needs to let others know what would be helpful to them.

Children

If the parents have other children, they will also have suffered a loss. They were looking forward to a little brother or sister. Children react differently to death depending on where they are developmentally. Explaining what happened to them is difficult. Caregivers aren't often in a position to discuss the loss with another child in the family. Usually the parents will wish to do this themselves, but may have little skill in how to do so. Also, they are grieving themselves, and are not operating at their fullest capacity. As a caregiver, offer to explore with them how to discuss the loss with a child.

There are some basic guidelines on how to do this.

First of all, explain what happened in terms the child can understand, trying to keep it simple and as straightforward as possible. Answer their questions openly and honestly, keeping in mind that children are often able to comprehend more than we give them credit for. They will, however, ultimately comprehend it in their own way. Don't answer questions they don't ask. It is a common mistake to give a child more information than what they asked for and more than they can handle at the time.

Gauge the child as to how involved they might want to be in saying good-bye to the baby. They may want to see the baby, they may not. A large part of a parent's job is to protect their child. However, in this situation, protecting the child too much will lead them to feel left out of the process. Let them know their options, and that they are capable of making their own decision. Respect their wishes, since doing so respects their individuality.

Avoid answers that might have a double meaning for the child. An explanation of "The baby got sick and died" may tend to make the child very fearful the next time they cough or don't feel well. Saying "The baby is sleeping," might frighten the child into not sleeping well. "God took the baby to heaven," may leave a child thinking that God snatched the baby away for some unknown reason, thereby eroding any sense of overall safeness the child might feel. "God wanted the baby in heaven because they were so special," can leave a child in a true double bind: "Did I not get taken because I'm not special enough? And, if I somehow do get special enough, does this mean I'll be taken then, too?" The best answer is one that is honest and simple.

Prepare the couple that, for right now anyway, their other children can be a curse and a blessing at the same time. Children will keep them occupied and focused on the living. But, at the same time, they will probably remind them of the baby in whose life they will never get to share. Also, grieving parents are under a great deal of stress as a result of coping with their pain, and having a child (or children) in the house often doesn't allow them spontaneous opportunity to grieve. This may cause additional stress, and in turn, cause a buildup of stress which often is expressed in less than healthy ways.

Children (younger children especially) are sensitive to what is going on in their environment, and they tend to take ownership of the emotions around them. As they do so, they will often act out in ways that are uncharacteristic. The already stressed parent may find themselves reacting to their child in ways that are equally uncharacteristic.

Parents may need to be reassured that a child who acts out under these circumstances is relatively normal. Their child is communicating their uncertainty in the only way they know how. Compare it to how a small child becomes unruly when they are overly tired. They don't have the capacity to tell you they are tired (and if you ask them if they're tired, they will deny it), so they simply act it out. Parents have to learn to translate the acting out to its true meaning: they're tired! The parent can then respond accordingly—using a soft tone of voice which reflects their understanding the child's weariness, while putting them to bed as soon as possible. Similarly, acting out after a case of a perinatal loss may mean that the child needs reassurance or needs some encouragement to talk about the issues that are confronting them.

Putting the situation into examples the parent can relate easily to (such as the one above) will help them better understand their child's needs under these very unusual circumstances. Stress the unusualness of the circumstances to the parents in order to disarm any defensiveness on their part. It will also assist them in keeping their child's behavior in its proper perspective.

Leaving the Hospital

Going home can be a difficult transition for the parent after a perinatal loss. Leaving the protective and caring environment of the hospital and facing the real world can be devastating.

They will be confronted with the fact that while their world has seemed to stop, the rest of the world has continued to go on. Even on the drive home they may become angry that the world has not stopped and noticed the passing of someone so important.

If they had a special place prepared for their baby before the loss, going home will be a painful reminder of that unoccupied place. Friends may want to dismantle the nursery for them, but this may actually leave the parents feeling even more helpless and abandoned. Caregivers should address the issue of the nursery with the parents. Let them know that they can take the nursery down when they are prepared to. For a time, they may want to leave it up to honor their baby's memory. It may even be a place where they can go to be "with" their baby.

Prepare the couple for confrontational situations they will not anticipate: telephone solicitors wanting to schedule appointments for baby pictures; baby magazines; mailings for baby products; and calls from diaper services. Insurance salesperson will call to discuss "family" insurance coverage. These intrusions can be aggravating under the best of circumstances, but now they will be painful. Often, they will feel like they are in a no-win situation. If they tell the person exactly what happened, are they revealing information which is none of the caller's business? However, if they don't tell what happened, they will feel as though they are invalidating their baby's life.

Prepare the parents for other uncomfortable situations they will face in the outside world. First of all, it will seem as though there are babies and pregnant women everywhere. This may be painful. Seeing a parent neglect or mistreat their child in a store will be even more disturbing than usual. Overhearing someone admire a baby will make them sad. Emotions will probably surface in embarrassing ways and places. Let them know that they need to be gentle and understanding with themselves. A burst of emotion in a public place isn't something they would do normally, but this isn't a normal situation.

A public place can also be a work setting. The decision of when to return to work is a difficult struggle for both parents. Working with others who are pregnant, or who offer little understanding of the loss can be difficult simply from the prolonged extent and proximity of the exposure in the work setting. Parents may need to hear a caregiver give them permission to take as much time away from work as they need. A patient who has an unsupportive employer may need a caregiver to become their advocate to such an employer. Physicians are in an excellent position to stress the need for additional recovery time that will facilitate the employee being able to return to the work setting at optimal efficiency.

Prepare parents for the fact that they will feel as though they have to endlessly retell their story, and that they may tire of it. It will also feel as though they are having to constantly explain themselves and what they're going through. Although this may be maddening and seem pointless, it is all part of the path to healing.

The Future

Grieving parents will probably tire of hearing the phrase "time heals all wounds." As a caregiver, do not use this saying. The reality is that time alone doesn't take the pain away and leading parents to believe this can cause them future conflict.

It is true, however, that with time, the *acuteness* of their pain will subside. If this happens to soon, it may feel like a betrayal of the baby. But, as they adapt to a new reality of life without their baby, the pain will begin to feel less intense and consuming. The pain will become more of a dull ache, although there may be times when it will seem more acute than others.

It is inappropriate to discuss the long term future to soon in the healing process. But, if you are a caregiver coming into contact with the parents as they are adapting to their new reality, discussing with them what to expect and what they can do now will be helpful.

The anniversary of the due date, the date the baby died, or other important dates relating to the baby, will probably bring back the pain. Again, running from the pain will seem natural for them, but at the same time it will seem like a betrayal. They need to be with the pain for a time as a way of honoring the baby.

They may need validation of their desire to spend time "with" their baby on special days (such as holidays). There are many things they can do to fulfill their need to honor their baby and not forget. Planning a picnic at the graveside or even a memorial service can do much to relieve the pain. Many things can be done to memorialize the baby: plant a tree or some other living thing. Name a star at the local planetarium: have the baby's name put on a brick, walkway or anything concrete and lasting. Most of all, encourage parents to use their imaginations and do anything that has meaning to them.

Future Pregnancy

A part of the future for a grieving couple is exploring the possibility of getting pregnant again. At some point in the grieving process the couple will begin to contemplate the possibility of accepting the risk of another pregnancy. There is great debate over recommended time frames between pregnancies. The medical condition of the mother obviously needs to be taken into account. However, with a perinatal loss, psychological/emotional considerations also need to be addressed.

It is of primary importance that the couple not proceed into a subsequent pregnancy until:

1) they have gotten enough emotional distance from their loss to be able to endure another pregnancy;
2) they are looking at another child as an enhancement to their lives, not something to give life meaning;
3) they no longer want to replace the baby that was lost (the baby they will never have), but they want another child (a different child);
4) they are now aware of the risks involved, and are willing to accept those risks as a part of being pregnant (and as a part of life); and
5) their support system is prepared to provide for their additional needs in a subsequent pregnancy.

Evaluating the extent of these five conditions can be difficult. The best approach is to openly and honestly discuss future pregnancy with the grieving couple at a time when they are prepared to even think about that possibility. Usually they will inquire, often of the obstetrician, when a subsequent pregnancy can be considered. This presents an excellent opportunity to assess the patients' overall preparedness.

A subsequent pregnancy can represent that the couple has truly moved on with their lives. Even if this is the case, however, a subsequent pregnancy after a loss will undoubtedly be a traumatic experience. As a caregiver, be prepared for the mother to need extra time from you as well as your assurance. Extra tests will be reassuring to her, so remaining open to the need for additional testing will be very important for you. For example, the mother may have the need to hear the baby's heartbeat at every visit. Always remember that pregnancy proceeds optimally when all aspects—medical, physical, psychological, and emotional—are addressed and equally balanced.

Sometimes meeting the mother's additional needs can be done relatively simply, or, it can get quite extensive. One obstetrician I know goes so far as to make a fetalscope available to patients who have had losses. This may be an extreme measure, but it does help patients feel more in control when they can hear a heartbeat whenever they have the need. A mother who has incurred a loss can often become desperate to hear a heartbeat, and it invariably happens at a time when you, the caregiver, have no additional time to give to search for one. The above-mentioned obstetrician's unique solution of providing fetalscopes addresses this office visit complication.

On an intellectual level, everyone involved may be aware that any feeling of control is actually only an illusion. But, if it is of comfort to the mother and allows her to proceed less anxiously with her pregnancy, this illusion is worthwhile.

Even under the best of circumstances, a subsequent pregnancy will be characterized by increased anxiety and fearfulness. Validating these reactions (i.e., letting patients know that this is natural and normal in a subsequent pregnancy) can prevent these responses from becoming obsessive. Helping patients to maintain a balance, and therefore keeping a subsequent pregnancy from being less of a nightmare of anxiety and helplessness, becomes a major part of the caregiver role.

Ceremonies

Our society, like most, has rituals that are held in great esteem. These rituals not only give us meaning and a sense of belonging, they often define us as a people as well as individuals.

We literally live and die by these rituals, and they often give us comfort at times of transition. Our society does not have any rituals specifically for the loss of the as-yet-born. Those who experience this loss are sometimes confused as to what to do because society doesn't have any set rules.

Unfortunately, this gives many people permission to advise the parents as to what to do. Even more unfortunate, is the fact that these mostly well-meaning people pass on to the parents their own programming as to what is expected and what is "right" or "wrong." For some parents, this advice, especially if it matches their own personal value system, might be a relief in that it gives them a sense of direction.

But the advice can just as easily conflict with the parent's personal beliefs and create more conflict. This experience heightens the already overwhelming confusion of perinatal loss. Helping parents to get in touch with their own needs will assist them in designing ceremonies or rituals that will meet those needs. Helping them can be as simple as asking, "What is it that you need in formalizing a goodbye for your baby?", "Do you want to have a service?", or "What do you want to say or have said for you at the service?" Once obtaining an answer about the basics, more detailed information can be filled in as they go.

At the same time, understand that some parents may find great solace in knowing what is expected, so that they can just comply with a structured follow-through. If this is the case, telling the parents what is customary, or what others have done in the past, will be helpful.

Some grieving parents may even have a need to have someone help them make arrangements, often a parent. But the caregiver must remind anyone else making these arrangements that they must keep in mind that the ceremony is not being done for themselves, but for the grieving parents.

A ceremony can be as simple or as complex as the individual situation or need. With an earlier loss, there may not be any remains. In this case, a simple memorial service could be held at a chosen location (church, memorial garden, public park, home, hospital, playground—whatever location will fill the need). A memorial service can be formally conducted by a pastor or minister, or more informal, even to the point of being conducted by the parents themselves. A service can be open to friends and family, or more intimate with only the parents in attendance.

If remains are available, a service will most likely incorporate interment. Cremation is an option many parents choose, and if so, ashes can be kept and taken home, or distributed at a location which has meaning to them (check with local authorities, as laws can apply in the the distribution or placement of human ashes). Often, in today's transient society, younger couples may not be living where they want to leave their baby's remains, knowing they will likely be moving away. Cremation becomes a viable option in that they can take the remains with them when they move.

With a later loss (especially after 20 weeks), funeral arrangements of some form may even be required. But, even funerals can be simple or elaborate. It can be as simple as a graveside service with only the parents attending, or elaborate enough to include visitation, viewing, interment, and a social function following. Again, fulfilling the needs of the grieving parents is the critical issue.

Within a ceremony itself, there are many ways of symbolically saying what is needed to be said. Releasing balloons with a message of love written on them (again, check local laws), symbolically burying a memento, wrapping an urn in a special blanket, placing a teddy bear on the marker of a grandparent, planting a tree, are all examples of symbolism that can be a part of a ceremony—they can even be the entire ceremony.

For any loss, a memorial service can provide solace and validation. An important piece of advice to give a grieving couple is that a public service can also be invalidating in that others may not understand nor accept the parents' grief or chosen methods of ceremony. Some may choose to not attend, or they may attend the service and send some messages of disapproval. Either way, it can be difficult. Advise parents that any form of ceremony they choose is for *their* benefit, and in deciding on the form of service, they need to first take care of themselves.

Ceremonies can also be held long after the loss occurs. You may be lucky enough to live in a community that holds annual services for specific deaths. A private memorial service held on a significant date can also provide a great deal of comfort. This date could be the baby's original due date, date of delivery, date of death (if known), or any other date that has special significance. This service could be a structured event or as casual as a picnic. Remember that grief and loss are individual experiences, so ceremonies can be equally individual.

Caregiver Issues

Physicians

Physicians are indeed on the front lines when it comes to medical tragedy. There is probably no more difficult task physicians have to deal with than death. And, death of the unborn is probably the most complex of deaths.

An obstetrician explained to me that he had once been asked what part of his job had the biggest impact on him. His reply was, "the losses." Probably not what the person asking the question expected to hear. But the answer illustrates the point that for the physician, a perinatal loss is also a loss for him or her.

Even if the loss is looked upon entirely from the standpoint of loss of a medical condition that was under your treatment, it's still a loss. As such, this loss can represent another loss—the loss of a patient. However, the permanent loss of the patient from your practice can not only be prevented, but if treated carefully, the situation can become a great asset.

This just points out that losses, and how they are handled, are important on several different levels. Losses are obviously important to the patient and have a great impact on them, but they also have great impact on the physician.

In my work of running a perinatal loss support group, I have come to know many obstetricians over the years. All seem to have one thing in common: they specialized in obstetrics because of the experience of bringing a new life into the world, and the resultant joy attached to the occasion. They all also agree that it is a demanding way to make a living and that the most difficult and demanding part of the profession is the losses.

In the structured support group that I run, I invite a local obstetrician to visit the group one night of the seven that the group meets. Their visit has a two-fold objective.

First, I want them to answer medical questions that parents may have that haven't been answered by their own doctor. Patients often feel a sense of loyalty to their doctor and don't want to ask questions that may be construed as questioning the doctor's competency. Also, due to circumstances, they may not have had time to fully discuss the situation with their doctor. Many times questions arise after the patient has been discharged from the doctor's care or from the hospital.

Secondly, I want the doctor's visit to my group to give the parents an opportunity to hear how a physician deals with loss. Patients often falsely see the physician as a medical robot with infinite medical wisdom and knowledge, but no feelings of their own.

The physician's visit to the support group also has a benefit for the physician. It gives the doctor an opportunity to relate to non-patients who have incurred losses. Being with non-patients, the physician is free to vent some frustrations with this part of the profession. How difficult it is, for example, to be in one exam room telling a mother that her baby has died and then moving on to the next patient and feeling the pressure to be cheerful while telling her she is having a picture perfect pregnancy. How difficult it is to be with a patient who has been compliant and responsible throughout her pregnancy, only to lose the baby just prior to delivery to an apparent cord accident. Or, how frustrating it is to have made correct calls in a difficult and demanding pregnancy and then lose the baby anyway to an opportunistic infection.

I have had many physicians relate to me that they benefitted from their visit to the group, despite the fact that they would not have thought so in advance. It again validates the point that talking about it *does* help.

Each physician I know has their own way of dealing with their patients' losses. At the same time they also know that it is their job to continue the quality of medical care needed throughout the loss, regardless of their own feelings. This is a difficult balancing act when feelings are intense.

There is a primary point to keep in mind when the feelings of loss are intense: don't fall into the trap of just avoiding the patient. Obstetricians are specialists, and as such only need to be present when it's called for medically. This can mean that you're only medically needed for a few brief visits and the actual delivery, with everything else being turned over to a competent nursing staff. But this situation has pitfalls that need to be noted.

It may sometimes be a reality in a busy labor and delivery unit that you are attending several patients simultaneously and don't have the extra time to give to a patient with a loss. But it may also be that in this intensely emotional situation, you just don't want to be there. Either way, this is a situation that, if not handled carefully, can strain the doctor/patient relationship, sometimes to the breaking point.

Keep in mind, as parents are experiencing their loss, their world has become frozen in time—very stark, very dark and foreboding. Their perspective of the world has become very black or white. As the physician, you become part of their world, and will be perceived in those black or white (bad or good) terms. To illustrate this point, the hundreds of couples whom I have dealt with who have had loses, seem to put their physicians into one of two categories: 1) they walk on water, or 2) they should be put against a wall and shot. This is only the patient's perception, but it is important to consider when the category you fall into is pretty much dependent on how your responded to your patient's needs.

One of the most important things for a physician to remember is that your patient is, like yourself, a person. The patient is not a set of symptoms, or a particular medical problem, or a procedure, but a person. And being a person who finds themselves in a loss situation, they have a great deal of emotion to deal with.

The patient needs to know that their physician is in emotional control, because they know they aren't. At the same time, however, they need to know that their physician cares about their loss, not just about their particular medical challenge. This, obviously, presents a challenge. It's a balancing act between showing the patient that you care about them as a person, and being distanced enough from the emotional nature of the situation to be objective and effective.

At the same time, remember that the patient has to look to the physician for answers and explanations. The physician is looked upon as the expert on what to do next. The patient will often ask for guidance, not only medically, but often psychologically/emotionally. As a result, the physician needs to anticipate these questions. If you're not prepared to give psychological or emotional guidance, be willing to admit that it is out of your realm. Admitting this helps the patient see you as more "real," more human, and at the same time more competent medically because you're perceived as a physician who knows their specialty.

At the point of loss, be careful to avoid technical or sterile language. To a mother who has just lost her entire future with her child, hearing you call it a "non-viable fetus," will likely cause a reaction. If you're lucky, it will be confusion, and if you're not, it will be anger. But from the patient's standpoint, either confusion or anger will lead to complications.

The parents need the use of "real" terminology; "baby," "died," "lived," etc. Later, when they struggle with the unreality of the situation, it will be helpful for them to remember you, the physician, using terms that made the situation a little more real. Remember, while you need to be emotionally disconnected, they have a strong need to be emotionally connected.

Initially, some patients might profess that they are not being emotionally effected by their loss. This may give the physician permission to validate this response so as to maintain the patient's, as well as their own comfort level. While this is understandable, don't forget that as caregivers, we are committed to the over-all well-being of the patient. Often this means that we do what the patient needs rather than what they want. In this particular situation, you can validate their emotional distance as what they need to be doing *now,* but let them know that later they may need to go back and emotionally revisit the circumstances.

Many physicians have difficulty saying “I'm sorry.” Many interpret this phrase as being an admission of guilt or wrongdoing, or at the very least negligence. Remember that “I'm sorry” is none of these. It is a way to communicate to the patient that you know the great impact this loss is having on them, and that you regret their having to go through it. “I'm sorry your baby died,” “I'm sorry this happened to you,” or “I'm sorry that you're having to go through this,” is phraseology that is actually more accurate.

If you find yourself still uncomfortable with the words “I'm sorry,” use “I regret” in its place. Even “I really wish this hadn't happened to you” can communicate the same sentiment. The physician needs to identify and empathize with the pain of the loss, but not take responsibility for either the loss or the pain.

It is important for patients to see their physician as competent, but not omnipotent. Keep in mind that being perceived as omnipotent may be ego-gratifying, but it backfires. If you are, indeed, all-powerful, then you should have been able to prevent the loss. If you, as a physician could have prevented the loss, then you must take responsibility for it. This notion produces conflict for both physician and patient. The physician feels guilty and the patient feels angry and betrayed. Communicating an emotional connection with patients will evaporate any perception of omnipotence, and generally disarm this potentially damaging conflict.

Later in a pregnancy, a loss often involves the need to induce labor. This can be a long and arduous process for all concerned. But, it also presents a valuable opportunity to give both physician and patient an opportunity to spend some time getting to know one another. It is a perfect opportunity for the physician to become a “real” person—to communicate a human-to-human concern for the patient's welfare.

It is also an opportunity for the physician to dominate the situation. This may assist the physician in perceiving they are in control, but it may not actually help the patient.

For example, during this time, a judgement call is often made concerning the amount of anesthetic medication the mother can be given. It is often believed that because the baby has already died, additional pain medication can be given to the mother to "help her through it." Although the physician may believe they are doing something humane for the mother, the patient must be given complete control of this situation.

I have worked with many mothers who regret their being so drugged during the delivery of their child that they don't even remember it. This represents to the mother an additional loss—the loss of the experience of childbirth. It also can compound an already complex bereavement situation. Not the least of these complications is the jealousy the mother eventually will feel toward the father because he has clear recollection of the birth, thereby magnifying the male vs. female conflict.

Having addressed the subject of gender differences, physicians indeed need to remember that although their patient is the mother of the child, the child also has a father. The father may or may not be as devastated as the mother, but it is important to remember that he, too, has incurred the loss of the future he was planning with that child. Sometimes, physicians will give much responsibility for the mother to the father by asking him "to take care of her." Other times, especially when the mother is not able to respond, the father must be asked to make decisions that need to be made. It is vital, however, to remind the father to take care of himself, to validate his loss, and to not give him so much to do that he de-focuses from his own pain and enters denial as a coping mechanism.

It is also important that physicians not look at their patients who have incurred losses as damaged or incompetent. They are badly injured, not damaged. They will require a lot of specialized care, gentleness, and understanding. Given that, they will heal.

It will, therefore, behoove the physician to guide the patient to any specialized care they require. Literature on perinatal loss needs to be available. Referrals to local support groups need to be made. There needs to be follow-up on the patient's emotional and psychological progress as well as their medical needs. You should have the names of therapists in the area who specialize in bereavement and grieving issues (or hopefully, a specialist in perinatal loss) in case referral needs to be made. A list of books written on the subject of perinatal loss should be made available to the patient.

It is a good idea to develop a packet of information that can be given to each patient who experiences a perinatal loss. You, as the caregiver, can go into as much of its detail as you and the patient are comfortable with. A packet of information gives the patient and the spouse an opportunity to go through the information when they are ready to. They will be much more receptive to the information when they don't feel it's being imposed on them. Sooner or later, they will be in need, and will want to know where to turn for help. Some will be able to get the help they need directly from the packet, others will require more. But it is best to give them access to the information now so that specifics are readily available to them at the time when they are ready.

Often, it is the physician who sees the patient throughout the entire grieving process. The physician is there when the loss first occurs, at the time when the patient is in shock and denial, or disbelief. Through the follow-up visits, the physician sees the patient through the painful adjustment period of trying to cope with the loss and its meaning. Finally, through re-connecting with a subsequent pregnancy, the physician sees the patient truly incorporate the loss into their life, and to their very understanding of the meaning of life.

The subject of subsequent pregnancy is an important one that will invariably arise between patient and physician. As the physician, you will be in touch with the patient's fears relative to any subsequent pregnancy. Often a physician will try to allay these fears by offering statistics and probabilities based upon a female of a certain age with these certain medical characteristics. While this information can be useful, being aware of these statistics does nothing to diminish the significance of the loss, or rarely does anything to diminish the fear attached to the subsequent pregnancy. As a physician, be careful to not minimize or invalidate a loss by focusing on a subsequent pregnancy. Doing so may alleviate your discomfort over a loss, but this process will be sensed by the grieving parent.

Another dynamic that can easily come into play is one in which the father, in his feeling of powerlessness, begins focusing on a future pregnancy as a remedy for the painfulness of the loss. The father may focus on a subsequent pregnancy in order to focus on something over which he perceives he has more control. Some physicians, especially males, have a tendency to align themselves with this mindset. However, this strategy will endear neither of them to the grieving mother. Physicians need to be aware of this particular dynamic and disarm it by identifying the issues involved, and if needed, relate them back to the father. Above all, do not allow yourself as a medical professional to get caught in this trap.

If you, as a physician, are mindful of the issues, and are fortunate enough to be aware of them, you will see, in time, a remarkable transformation. Before your eyes, a person of true depth and beauty will emerge from all the ugliness and pain. It is, in a sense, a new beginning – the birth of a whole new person.

Nurses

Nurses are involved with perinatal loss to a depth that can not be equaled by any other field. Nurses have extended, direct patient contact at the most difficult time imaginable. You, as a nurse, must constantly balance the patient's medical, psychological, and emotional needs at a time when all three are demanding attention. Sometimes these needs can become one, simply addressed with a touch, a hug, or a shared tear. These are the special gifts that nurses give, and their impact is more powerful than most realize.

I have broken down nursing involvement into different areas of patient contact where the situations, and the issues, tend to be slightly different. However, there are some basics that will be a part of each nursing situation.

In the midst of a perinatal loss crisis, parent focus tends to narrow and each event is intensely experienced. What that means to the nursing professional is that what you do can, and probably will, significantly affect them. Since you *will* make a difference, endeavor to make the difference a positive one. You cannot take away the pain of the loss, but you can attach a memory of caring to it.

In the initial contact, caring and compassion is what will make the biggest impression. You need to give the mother or couple permission to experience their feelings. Communicate to them clearly and concisely, telling them: 1) who you are, 2) that you know what has happened, 3) that you know what to do medically, and 4) that you care.

Be genuine. This is a difficult situation for everyone, and it's OK to express that. Avoid phrases like "At least...," or "It could have been...." This is a vain attempt to fix their pain. The sooner *you* accept that you can't do that, the sooner *they* will recognize that you can't.

You will be there in the midst of the emotional eruption. You will likely witness an outpouring of guilt, shame, anger, sadness, hopelessness, and possibly other emotions. Let your patient know their feelings are natural, normal and even expected. But, at the same time, you may need to let them know that you are there because of their medical condition, and that they may (depending on the level of their emotionality) have to temporarily hold their feelings in check until their immediate medical condition can be resolved.

Stating this boundary needs to be done with compassion. For the most part, patients will comply when told what they need to be doing, especially if they understand they will be able to emote when it's more suitable to do so.

As a nurse, you are also in an excellent position to identify support persons for the grieving parents. These people could be friends, family, or even other professional caregivers (social workers, clergy, therapists, support group leaders, etc.). Professional caregivers are community resources, and information about them can be given. (Therefore, it's a good idea if you familiarize yourself with these resources.)

If the support persons you identify are friends or family, make sure they are aware that they now play an important role in the parents lives. Guide them as to what to do to help the couple. If you're not sure how to guide them, refer them to other resources. Let them know that in their role as a support person, they may need to educate themselves as to how to best help the grieving parents. Make them aware that one way in which they can support the parents would be to gather community resource information. This not only gives them something to do (and addresses their feeling of helplessness), but also makes the information more readily available to the parents when it's needed.

Emergency Room Nurses

An emergency room nurse will be in contact with perinatal loss under a variety of different circumstances. An expectant mother who is experiencing bleeding or cramping will often come through the emergency room. Sometimes these symptoms don't predispose a loss, and the patient is sent home. However, these are sometimes symptoms of a loss about to occur, in the process of occurring, or having just occurred. These are three distinctively different situations.

If the symptoms indicate a loss is eminent, the mother is in great fear of losing her baby. She is also feeling guilt for what she may have done—or not have done—to cause this to be happening to her. Obviously, the medical problem needs to be addressed first. However, understand that the fear and the guilt are simultaneous experiences, and that one is feeding the other. Also, keep in mind that fear is often expressed as anger. The anger may be directed at society, the hospital, the baby's father, or at you, the nurse. Don't react to the anger, respond to it. Address the fear behind the anger, not the anger. If the mother can more accurately express her fear, she will be less in conflict within herself and therefore less volatile and more compliant.

Here are some helpful hints to remember when trying to address your patient's fear rather than their anger. First, remember that if you react to their anger, you are doing just what the word says: you are *re*-acting their anger. All you are doing is copying their initial action. There is no individual thought on your part in your action, and you are not being you—you're just *re*-acting them. Once this happens, the patient's perception will be that you are the one that has the problem, not them. This will be somewhat true in that they have successfully given their anger to you, and you now possess it.

Second, validate their right to be angry. Tell them it's OK to lash out, that you understand their anger. Tell them that if you were experiencing what they are now going through, you'd be angry too. If possible, briefly relate to them a time when you were in a stressful situation, and you, too, lashed out in anger. Once they know you understand their need to be angry, the strength of the anger will diminish, and you will have defused it. Then they will be more open to discussing their anger and the fear behind it.

Don't try to dismiss their anger by defending the person, place, or action on which they are focusing their anger. If you fall into this trap, you will have immediately alienated yourself from the patient. You will have become one of *them,* and as such, you will have earned your portion of their anger. If this happens, you will find it nearly impossible to re-connect with the patient, and will do well to call for another nurse to care for them.

Remember that the patient is looking to you, the nurse, for answers. They will read your every move and facial expression. Be aware of this. Prepare them for the possible outcome, "I'm concerned...," "I realize this is hard...," These phrases are honest and will feel better for everyone than pretending would.

If the symptoms indicate a loss in progress, and the loss actually occurs in the emergency room, the mother will probably respond differently than the above. Fear is less likely to be present because the worst thing they could imagine happening, is happening. If fear is expressed, it is more likely the fear of personal life or safety, not the baby's. (This, in turn, may bring up feelings of guilt for her.) Much more likely emotions under these circumstances are guilt, sadness, hopelessness, and sometimes, apathy (best described as a complete lack of emotion). These emotions can be portrayed in a variety of ways; "I knew I should (shouldn't) have...," "Now that this has happened, there is no point in going on," or noticeable silence and uncomfortably avoiding eye contact.

Again, responding to the underlying emotion, rather than reacting to the behavior, will help best defuse the situation. "I know your emotions are running wild right now, but stay 'with' me and we'll get through it" will do much to convey important messages on several levels: validation of the emotional confusion; hope of there being another side to this intensity; and knowledge that they are not going to have to go through it alone.

Should the mother appear apathetic, don't think she doesn't actually care. She is experiencing shock over what has just happened in, and to, her life. She is still in denial as to the full impact of the loss on her life. She is overwhelmed and has shut down in order to process her circumstances. Don't try to shake her into reality. She's not ready for it. She will begin feeling again when she is able to and not before. Communicate to her your caring and concern for her and the father, and trust that they will record it and respond to it when they are able to. However, that may be after they are discharged, and you may not get to experience it with them.

If the loss has already occurred by the time they arrive in the emergency room, damage control is your priority. Medically, the physical damage needs to be dealt with. This needs to be done with as much caring and compassion as the setting will allow. Most often, they will at some level know what has just happened. They may still have a reaction to being told the harsh reality, so the news needs to shared as gently as possible.

Emotionally they are experiencing a great deal of turmoil, but be careful to think of them (or treat them) as injured, not damaged. Don't be condescending or minimizing—if you do, you're treating them like emotional morons, and they will react accordingly. Use gentle language and tone of voice. "I know this is overwhelming..." will communicate caring, empathy, and add validity to the enormity of the loss. "...Right now we need to be concerned about treating the physical parts of the problem" will communicate that there are other parts of this than the physical, they're not going to have to go through it alone, and that later there will be opportunity to deal with the rest of it.

Keep in mind that most of those whose losses come through the emergency room will be in and out in a very short period of time. The rapidness of the situation will add to the unreality of it. Prepare them for this by talking about it. Question the couple to see if you can discover their support system and encourage them to utilize it. They may be numb now, but they will remember it later when they need to. Remember the family will leave the hospital injured and you want to try to insure that emotional infection doesn't set in.

Under these circumstances, also keep in mind that a mother who incurs an early term loss will often be in and out of the emergency room before it really occurs to anyone what the patient actually lost. It is important that these grieving mothers don't fall through the cracks and disappear, never having their loss validated or addressed. Remember that society as a whole tends to devalue an early term loss, so don't fall into that mold. It will be helpful to the patient to be informed that: "Generally, society doesn't fully recognize your loss, so many people may tell you it's no big deal. But if it is a big deal to *you,* it *is* a big deal. Don't let them minimize your loss." Under these circumstances, a follow-through is essential. Further detailed information on how a follow through should be made can be found in the Hospital Social Workers section.

In some instances, the situation arises in which the mother's life is in danger, and the difficult decision is confronted as to whose life to save, mother's or baby's. Medically, this decision is usually very clear. However, by placing a higher priority on saving the mother's life, a paradox of guilt of monumental proportions can be created. Gratefully, the mother is often either heavily sedated or in extreme pain and not in a lucid state to make this decision for herself. She is probably not aware of the decision being made for her, or being carried out, and consequently will not interfere in the process. However, be aware that the mother will not escape guilt under these conditions, and her guilt will be as overwhelming as the situation itself. Follow through is essential under these conditions.

Nurses in Labor and Delivery

Often, by the time a mother reaches Labor and Delivery, the baby has already died. If this is the case, the parents are either numb and just going through the motions, or they are emotional wrecks. What was to be a joyous occasion, will now be sheer agony—in many ways that agony has just begun for them.

Medically, prepare for the delivery the way you would under more happy circumstances, but make certain the couple stays informed as to what is going on around them. Keep in mind that the couple may not have had Lamaze training, so ask. If they have not attended Lamaze, and you have time, you may want to coach them. If there is not time, give them instructions as you go.

If the mother is in the very early stages of labor, or is just now being induced, prepare them for the choices they will be making (for example, whether to see, hold, bathe, or dress the baby). Don't put off until later what you can prepare them for now. Validate what they might be feeling, "I know this is overwhelming...," or "before the contractions become more intense...," and then cover some of the decisions they will be making. The very word "before" implies both that it *will* happen, and emphasizes the need to prepare for it.

Also prepare for a possible rapid finish to labor. When it is known that the baby has died, the mother is often kept more heavily medicated and may not be fully aware of the early signs of delivery being imminent. Find out if this is their first child, since if it is, they are now probably more afraid of delivery than "normal" first-time parents. Be reassuring, comforting and confident.

Often, in an induction situation, there is a great deal of waiting time. Use the time wisely. Let them know this is a horrible situation, and you regret them having to experience it. In doing so, you're preparing them for how their situation is different from other deliveries.

At the same time, prepare them for the similarities to a more "normal" birth. Share with them what to expect after the delivery. Talk about their fears and try to reassure them as much as possible. Find out their feelings about seeing or holding the baby. Describe for them what they might see (what the baby might look like). Describe for them what "normal" tissue changes might have taken place. Offer them the choice of contact with the baby and let them know they can change their mind at any time. For example, let them know they can wait to make the decision until after the delivery, so they can be told exactly what they will be seeing.

In reference to seeing/holding the baby, ask if they have ever seen anyone who has died. Remember, this might be their first experience with death and they may be extremely frightened. This may be a good time to find out about their support system: is there anyone whom they would like to be here with them? Is there anyone else in the family who would like to see or hold the baby? If you find out who the support system might be, try to talk to them. They may be able to reassure or calm the couple.

At the same time, be aware of any negative effects family or other support persons may have on the couple. You may try to counter or at least minimize this negative or unhealthy impact by talking to them. If this is out of your realm, or, if the family appears to be extremely dysfunctional to the point of disrupting the entire process, call a social worker or someone more specifically trained in family dynamics.

Inform parents of all the different mementos they might want, and the power of these things. Ask if they have named the baby. Since a name is what gives each of us our individuality, naming the baby is probably one of the most powerful remembrances available to a couple. Mementos include footprints, handprints, pictures, certificates, a lock of hair, or *anything* that has touched the baby. Any of these things will later help an unreal situation be more real. Most hospitals have a set protocol for the collecting and storing of these mementos, including who is responsible for doing so. If this is not the case, it will be helpful for one person to accept this task, specifically relinquishing it to someone should there be a shift change. (If there is no protocol for this in your hospital, nursing administration needs to be informed so one can be established.)

For most couples, the most powerful memory is actually seeing or holding the baby. Gently encourage them to see their baby, but do *not* insist. If they are afraid of what they might *see,* describe the baby, tell them what you saw. Taking a picture and showing them the picture may reassure them. Tell them you'll clean the baby, and dress or wrap the baby, if that is their need. On the other hand, don't automatically assume they would want you to do these things—they may want to bathe and dress the baby themselves. Offer this as an alternative.

Don't just take care of everything for them. Let them participate and do what they have the need or desire to do. Soon, they will be confronted with the fact that they will not be able to do any of the things they were looking forward to doing. Then they will be grateful for what they could do when they had the chance.

In presenting the baby, be gentle but not protective. Describe the physical appearance of the baby. Talk about "normal" tissue deterioration. Keep in mind that what may be difficult for you to view, is their *baby.* Medical professionals usually tend to be over-protective of families in perinatal losses.

A nurse once told me a story about a particularly difficult delivery she participated in. The obstetrician gave strict instructions that the mother was not to be shown her baby, since it was delivered in pieces. After the delivery, the mother was agonizing over not having seen her baby, even though she was informed as to the baby's physical condition. She finally convinced the nurse to describe the baby in minute detail. After the description, the mother's reaction was: "She was only in *two* pieces?" The mother had apparently imagined the worst: dozens of small unidentifiable fragments. The mother's relief was so evident that she was allowed to see her baby, thereby preventing an extremely complicated bereavement situation.

In taking a picture, try to warm up the setting. Hospital lighting tends to be harsh so try to compensate for it. Wrap the baby in something that is the least clinical you can find. Put something in the picture to give a reference of size (for example, your hand or a small toy). A picture of the baby being lovingly held by another nurse would warm any picture.

As the loss is taking place, be aware that the parent(s) may get in touch with previous losses. Loss often puts us in touch with loss. Previous perinatal losses or other death experiences may come to mind. You may even want to mention that this is a common occurrence before it happens since they may welcome the opportunity to talk about it further.

Prepare them for some of the other decisions they will be faced with. For example, they may not even have considered that they will have to make arrangements for disposition of their baby. Or, the physician may have discussed doing an autopsy: they may want to talk about this with you, since they probably have bonded with you and look to you for guidance.

Most importantly, show support for their decisions, even if you may personally disagree with them.

Post Partum Nurses

As the couple is moved to Post Partum, they are experiencing another loss, that of the L&D nurses they have probably bonded with. Understand that the bereaved parents may be distant and hard to reach. They may be acutely withdrawn or they may be angry, but most assuredly, by now they are completely overwhelmed by the recent events in their lives. Acknowledge this; say it. Every time the couple hears it, it validates for them the immensity of their loss.

Acknowledge their feelings. If they are angry, for example, don't react to their anger, but let them know it is OK to be angry.

Acknowledge that is difficult for them to be in post partum. Prepare them for the sounds of other babies and the happy faces and babies they will see in the hallways.

Ask them about their support systems. Find out whether or not they would prefer to receive calls by letting them know that the phone can be taken out of the room if they want. At the same time, ask who it is they can count on to be there for them. Find out who they need to tell about their loss and if there is someone else whom they want, and is willing, to do the calling for them. Let them know that it is acceptable to send an announcement if they wish.

Monitor food and fluid intake (depending on medical circumstances) and sleep patterns. These can be good indicators of pathological grief in its beginning stages.

Now is the time to begin discussing what they might expect

from this point onward. They will walk out of the hospital feeling as though their world has come to an end. As they drive home, they will realize that the world has already moved on without them. They will feel out of sync for a while.

Prepare them for encounters with casual acquaintances: the cashier at the grocery store, or the dry cleaner clerk who notices and says "Oh, you had your baby!" Let them know these difficult situations will arise and to think about how they will want to handle them. Model different ways to answer the question: "Yes, we did have the baby. Unfortunately, she died before (or 'shortly after') she was born." Let them know that family and friends who care about them will tend to expect them to be over the loss long before they really are. Explain that grief is not something we get over, like a cold, but is a process we move through, and that their relatives and friends have not been affected as they have been.

Prepare them for the fact that, they as a couple, will grieve differently simply because they are different genders and different individuals. This will usually become evident within two to three weeks and it will tend to add stress to an already stressful situation. Explain that each of them will need support besides that which they can provide for each other.

Ask if they have a nursery already set up in their home. Talk about their options. They can have someone else take it down for them if it would be to painful for them to handle right now. Or, they can leave it until they are ready to take it down themselves. The key is that they should do whatever will serve their needs the most.

If you're comfortable in doing so, be open to discussing the rituals to come, such as a funeral or memorial service. By this point, someone (physician, social worker, clergy) should have broached the subject of whatever ritual might be a part of their particular situation and they may want someone else's advice. If you're aware of what other couples have done to address these rituals, be open to sharing this information with them.

Let them know that anniversary dates (date of the delivery, the due date, date of conception) will be difficult. Give them permission to honor their baby and themselves on those dates.

You are in an excellent position to suggest support groups or make referrals to counselors knowledgeable in grief or perinatal loss. Find out how they feel about attending a support group. If they are curious, tell them the benefit of being in a room with a group of people who have also experienced what they have just experienced. If they are resistant, just give them the information and tell them they can use the information at a time when they are ready. Be careful to use "when" they are ready, not "if" they want to. These are two very different messages.

Most of all, convey to them that they need to trust and honor themselves. They will know what they need to do for themselves if they will allow themselves to listen.

Nurse Managers/Discharge Planners

As nurse managers, you need to be familiar with the previous three nursing sections. Not only do you have to be prepared when you personally come in contact with bereaved parents, but nurses that you supervise *will* come to you with questions and you have to be able to guide them through difficult situations. At the same time, recognize that you have the difficult task of always having to balance the needs of the patient, your nursing staff, and the hospital. Your task of supporting your nurses comes in making sure they are well trained in the unique issues of perinatal loss. This helps to insure that the needs of the patient will be met, and, as a result, so will the needs of the hospital.

Discharge planning becomes a critical component of the overall care of the patient. It is at this point that the long-term needs of the patient need to be addressed. Will there be some form of follow-up by the hospital, and who will make the follow-up call? How does the couple plan to address their now changed needs? Has support group information been provided?

As I have observed in another section, keep in mind that the couple's focus will narrow and become very black or white (meaning everything will be good, or bad, and there will be no in between). If the couple perceives the hospital as having met their needs, and done so in a compassionate and caring way, there will likely not be any negative backlash. From a risk management standpoint this is obviously critical, but also remember that it is equally critical from a humane standpoint. Follow through after discharge can make an enormous difference on both levels.

Office Nurses

If the loss occurs (or is first realized or suspected) in the office setting, pay attention to relevant parts in the previous nursing sections. Most of all be aware and sensitive to the needs of the couple or mother.

If the loss occurred in the hospital, you are seeing the mother or couple for follow-up visits. Make sure you validate the power of what they have experienced. This can be done by simply letting them know how you have been affected. Let them know that you are saddened by their loss and that you care.

If at all possible, when they come in for follow-up appointments, try to schedule them at a time when the waiting room isn't full of bulging mothers. If this isn't possible, perhaps you could let them wait in another room where they won't be exposed to the other patients. If neither of these are viable options in your office, explain that you know it's difficult for them to come in with all the expectant mothers in the waiting room and that you wish it could be different for them.

As you continue to see them, gauge their progress in the grieving process. Are they letting go? Are they moving on? If you see signs they are stuck in the grieving process, discuss it with their doctor. Share with the doctor your observations and what the parents have told you. Remember, you are often the doctor's eyes and ears. Many times, grieving parents will share with you what they may not tell the doctor. If you're not sure of what signs may indicate that they are stuck in the grieving process, refer to the Therapist/Counselor section later in this book.

Be aware that parents will move through the grieving process at different paces. Men and women grieve differently. If the mother comes in alone and confides in you that she feels distant from her husband, she is telling you that they are at different points in the grieving process. Share with her the differences in male vs. female grieving styles and reinforce they are both doing it in their own meaningful way.

At the same time, be listening for signs of the marital relationship being torn apart. Although there is no empirical data available, some feel that the percentage of marriages that fail after experiencing trauma, such as a perinatal loss, is high. If you hear signs of marital conflict arising, discuss with the doctor the possibility of a referral to a therapist.

Be careful not to make judgmental remarks about how long the grief process is taking. These comments will be interpreted as they're not getting over it fast enough. Remember that we all grieve at our own pace. On the other hand, if there are signs of the grieving process taking on extreme proportions, discuss this with their doctor. More than likely, the doctor will already be aware of it by this point, but never assume the doctor already knows.

Eventually you will see positiveness return to their lives. You will hear them beginning to play with the idea of a future pregnancy, or even coming in for an appointment and being told they are pregnant once again. This is a bittersweet situation. They are happy about being pregnant again, but it's also a reminder of the baby who was lost. Be aware of this conflict, and how fearful it is for them to be faced once again with a situation that ended so horribly for them once before. Don't try to reassure them by telling them it won't happen again, or that everything will be OK, because you don't know that. The best thing you can do is validate that this is an anxious time for them, and that you (personally, and as an OB practice) will be there for them. By saying this, they will see that their anxiety is expected and natural, that someone else empathizes with what they are going through, and that they aren't alone. Of course, simply knowing these things will probably not make their anxiety disappear. But, it probably will insure that their anxiety won't become pathological and jeopardize the pregnancy.

Be aware that they have undergone great change in the processing of their previous loss. Their outlook on life itself has likely changed. In addition to losing their baby, parents often also lose that sense of being in control of what happens in their lives. This issue intensifies as they begin to face a subsequent pregnancy and beyond. They probably realize that even if they deliver a healthy baby they still aren't going to be anxiety-free, because they know how little they are in real control of life. Validate the courage that it took to face this fear and the risks attached to another pregnancy. In this way, you're giving them positive feedback just when they need it the most.

Most of all, be supportive, understanding, caring and validating. As a patient moves through the process of change associated with a loss, knowing they are cared for will not only tremendously ease the burden, but will actually facilitate their growth.

Therapists / Counselors

One of the major goals of therapy is to help individuals resolve conflict within their lives. As a therapist, you facilitate the process of growth and assist in reaching a place of peacefulness from a place that's full of conflict. Even under the best of conditions, this is a complicated task. Bereavement, in its basic elements, presents a complex plethora of issues, and complicated bereavement offers even that much more of a challenge. Perinatal loss presents unique and complex issues that if not resolved can lead to serious pathology.

If a grieving mother or couple is referred to you, the first task is to assess their current mental well-being. Is this person experiencing expected responses to the situation? In other words, are they going about the task of mourning their loss and doing so in an expected format and time frame?

William Worden in his landmark work *Grief Counseling and Grief Therapy: A Handbook for the Mental Health Practitioner* talks about the tasks of mourning and what to look for as signs of an aborted task.

The first task of mourning is to accept the reality of the loss. Elizabeth Kubler-Ross talks about shock and denial as the first stages of the grieving process. In the immediacy of the loss, being in the stage of shock and denial is often the only thing that helps a person deal with ab overwhelming situation. You may even hear people actually say: "I can't believe this is happening!" This is an expected reaction. The mind, which may have a limited capacity to comprehend the situation, becomes overloaded and shuts down. As soon as the mind can break the situation down into more comprehendable pieces, the bereaved can safely move on and begin accepting the reality that the loss has truly taken place.

The sign of an aberrant task would be *to continue* not believing that the loss has, indeed, taken place. The language evidencing this could be as subtle as minimizing the loss, "I can't believe I'm still crying over such a little thing." Conversely, it can be as severe as not even recalling events surrounding the loss, or, even believing they are still pregnant. Other indications of continued denial include:

- not being able to even speak about the baby;
- being unwilling or unable to part with, or even move, possessions of the baby;
- not being able to visit the gravesite or participate in ceremonies of closure.

At the same time, however, keep in mind that minimizing the loss is common in perinatal loss, especially with earlier miscarriages. It is also common with fathers who had not fully bonded with the baby. Understanding the basis for the denial is one of the central issues to be considered.

Beginning to experience the pain of the loss is the next task of mourning. With a perinatal loss, this pain is the ache of not having the baby to hold—the emptiness left by the absence of the child. The expression of this pain is often tears.

Probably the most difficult part of the grieving process is allowing oneself to fully experience the pain. The pain can be so excruciating that people will often run from it. It is, after all, instinctual to avoid pain. Only humans allow, even sometimes encourage, ourselves to experience pain knowing there is a benefit forthcoming.

As a therapist, often the task is to assist patients experience their pain while in the safety of your office. Some patients are reluctant even there. Determining whether they are expressing their emotionality somewhere else or are totally shut down affectively is a focal task of therapy. Should you find they meet the DSM-IV criteria for depression, treatment needs to begin immediately. This is a complex bereavement situation and depression left untreated can quickly lead to more serious pathology.

Obtaining a comprehensive psycho-social can be essential in determining a history of depression, low self-esteem, and persistent guilt—all indications that grief will be difficult for this parent. A mother who has a history of dysthymia, for example, will need careful observation, support and guidance through the grieving process. Obtaining background information can also be helpful in determining if there are any radical changes in lifestyle brought about by the loss, another indicator of pathological grief.

An uncommon but troublesome indication of complicated mourning is a parent who begins to experience symptoms similar to those associated with the deceased. For example, the mother of a baby diagnosed as having died of congestive heart failure, begins complaining of chest pains with no previous history of such symptoms. Upon medical examination, no medical basis is found for such pain. This indicates more serious pathology, a somatoform disorder, not bereavement, and needs to be treated accordingly.

The next task of mourning is for the bereaved to adjust to an environment in which the deceased is missing. With a perinatal loss, this is a particularly difficult task. When alive, the baby's presence was nebulously a part of the parent's environment. Therefore, after death, the baby's lack of presence is not that much different. Also complicating this task is the fact that the baby was more directly a part of the mother's environment, so she will miss the baby's presence much differently than the father. The father may not have bonded to the baby, and so he doesn't feel the need to readjust to an environment in which the baby is no longer a part. This will, in turn, cause further conflict between the parents.

The biggest indication of parents working on the task of adjustment is their willingness to go on with their lives differently. A sign of noncompliance would be attempts at trying to keep the baby a part of their world in the present. Pay attention to their language, and listen for references to the baby being made in the present tense.

Often, part of a couple's adjustment to a new and different environment is dealing with other losses that may not be so obvious at first.

One example could be a situation in which the baby was deformed or grotesque in some way—a situation that is relatively common in perinatal loss. This circumstance can represent two losses: the loss of the child they actually lost, and the loss of the child they *thought* they had.

Another example is the loss of naiveness or innocence. Most couples suffering a perinatal loss, for obvious reasons, tend to be younger, and often the loss is the first realization of actually how little we are in control of our own lives. Unless they have confronted tragedy early in life, most young adults usually mature with the concept that life is pretty orderly: you grow up, you go through school, you meet the right person, you get married, you work, you buy a house, you have children, you get old, your children have children. Eventually, at the end of a long and fulfilled life, death comes. Pretty neat and tidy.

But real life is not so orderly, and younger couples can find themselves wrestling with this concept because of the perinatal loss. Helping them cope with this loss of control will be a major issue, even if they don't really acknowledge it.

The final task of mourning is to emotionally relocate the deceased and move on with life. The bereaved need to be able to love life, love others, and still hold that loving place for the baby that will always be solely theirs. This has to do with moving on, having meaningful relationships, and allowing meaningful situations to be a part of their life.

Signs of incompletion of this task of mourning is the patient who does not love, or has no meaningfulness to life because the deceased is not a part of their life. In other words, the patient ruminates that the only meaningful relationship in their life was the one they had with their baby. This, again, is best defined as clinical depression and needs to be treated as such.

It has been my experience that, under ordinary circumstances, the biggest task of the therapist will be to help the couple understand differences between male and female, as well as individual, grieving styles. In no other loss are these differences so pronounced and so inherently a part of the situation itself.

It is commonly accepted that those couples who have similar coping styles and more open communication will adjust more easily to perinatal loss. It is often the task of the therapist to help parents express their feelings about the loss in a form that is easily understood by the other. Most importantly, explore their feelings of fear and guilt. (A more in depth discussion of these differences has been covered in section one).

A therapist needs to take on the role of guide in the journey of grief. Ask along the way, as any good guide would, what it is that the person making the journey needs. Do not presume to know, for we all make the journey differently. A guide doesn't make the journey *for* the traveler but makes the journey *with* the traveler. A good guide has made the journey themselves, knows what helped them find their way, and shares those insights. A good guide also knows that the traveler may have to stumble and fall in order to really appreciate the true beauty that lies at the destination.

Support Groups

I have purposefully included this section on support groups under the heading of Therapists/Counselors. I don't mean to suggest that support groups should only be run by trained professionals, but it is a recognition that these are complex issues. Anyone facilitating a support group for perinatal loss needs to be fully aware of pertinent issues and be cognizant of the signs of someone who isn't moving through the stages of the grieving process. For the psychological welfare of all of the participants, the knowledge of what appropriate action to take is essential.

Support groups for perinatal loss take on the characteristics of one of two distinct formats: 1) unstructured and open; 2) structured and closed. Both formats have inherent strengths and weaknesses, and both are appropriate styles for addressing the issues of perinatal loss. Since both provide for distinctly different needs, the two formats are a good complement to one another. In the community of which I am a part, there are currently two support groups operating—one of each style. It's a complimentary relationship and much cross-referral is done.

Anyone interested in beginning a support group in their area needs to investigate several things. First of all, what is the need? (What is the local volume of losses? Is there sufficient support from the professional community to keep a group operating? Are there any other groups currently running in your area?) Second, what is the level of participation you are willing to extend, and what is the level of your training? Third, what type of group would best fit your therapeutic style and the needs of the participants who would use your support group?

Anyone running a support group holds a great responsibility to those in need, so providing a quality experience is essential.

Unstructured/Open Support Group. This style of support group is on-going, usually meeting at regular, consistent intervals throughout the year (a specified day every week or every month, for example). While there is often a format that is observed, the group is only loosely controlled by a facilitator. The facilitator usually opens the meeting, then turns the meeting over to those present to openly discuss their particular situation and what they may be experiencing at the present time. It is very much an open-forum style of discussion, with those present free to participate to their individual level of comfort.

The "open" label of this type of support group refers to two things. The first is the open-forum style of the group itself, while the other refers to the open-enrollment as regards to new participants coming into the group. This on-going style encourages participants to join at any time. This is an advantage for grieving parents in that they may join the group whenever they are ready to face such a situation—the time of their greatest need. It is also advantageous for those couples who need the more long-term support that is provided by such a group. Long-term attendance tends to strengthen relationships between participants, and thereby continues the support system beyond the group. There are also advantages for newly bereaved parents to seeing those who have worked beyond their pain and have survived, and this format allows people in all stages of their grief to participate.

The down side of the unstructured/open group, however, is that some participants may grow co-dependent on the group and may not move on in their grieving process. These parents may continue to attend the group and re-hash the same issues at each meeting for an extended period of time. They may indeed be stuck in a particular stage of grief. If allowed to dominate a group, they can keep others stuck, slow down other's progress, or alienate those who are progressing in their grief. There is the danger that some parents will then not return to the group even though they might have the need. It has, after all, become another uncomfortable experience.

The facilitator of such an unstructured/open group needs to be trained in the group process, the uniqueness of the issues, and knowledgeable of the signals indicating an unhealthy grieving process. They must also be knowledgeable of alternative resources for those participants who need them.

Structured/Closed Support Group. This style of support group is very different from the unstructured/open group. The structured group meets for a specified time period, usually a certain number of weeks. There is a specific structured exercise for each meeting. Each exercise tends to build on the exercise from the week before. The exercises are designed to assist participants as they progress through the stages of grief, while they gain a greater understanding of the grieving process itself. The structured group is a combination of teaching, open-forum discussion, homework, and processing specified topics.

Examples of discussion topics and exercises include:

- unique issues of this loss;
- grief as a process;
- male vs. female grieving styles;
- impact of the loss on the marital relationship;
- object linkage (participants encouraged to bring mementos to group);
- writing letters to the baby;
- reading those letters aloud in group;
- how to discuss-the loss with friends and family;
- "wearing" the loss in public;
- how to discuss the death with siblings of the baby;
- impact of the loss on self-esteem;

- medical questions and answers (local obstetrician present);
- addressing fears of another pregnancy;
- homework designed to assist the couple in moving on (having a date, for example); and
- discussions of how sexuality may be affected.

Structure is not only provided by having specified topics for each night, but it is also provided by beginning and ending the group in a formatted way. For example, a poem or reading tailored to the topic of each individual session can be used for a closing. Or, a ritualistic closing—such as forming a circle and reciting an appropriate phrase—lends structure. There may even be a combination of the two.

Structure is also provided by the level of guidance taken by the group facilitator. In a structured group, the facilitator needs to balance his or her leadership role while allowing the group to become cohesive and lead itself. As a result, this style of group necessitates a highly trained facilitator. It also requires a high level of participation, both within and outside the group, in terms of planning.

The "closed" part of the label for this style of group refers to the fact that this group has a specified beginning and an ending, usually running for a certain number of consecutive weeks. Once the group begins it is closed to new participants. Everyone who participates in the group begins and ends at the same time.

The advantages of a structured/closed group are that with a specified beginning and end, participants get a sense of finiteness to their pain. They will often enter the group believing they will be over it in the number of weeks that the group lasts. What they discover, however, is that the group facilitates healing, and while they are in less acute pain at the end of the group, they have not forgotten (gotten over it). Another advantage is that a strong group identity is developed when all participants move through the process together. And, with a specified ending date, there is the opportunity to "graduate," thereby providing a structured sense of completion, accomplishment, and of moving on. All of these sensations are greatly needed in the circumstance of perinatal loss.

A disadvantage of the structure/closed group is that if a couple's loss is out of sync with the group, they may have to wait a long period of time for the next group to begin. This could leave them feeling unsupported in the interim. Another disadvantage is that some couples may need more ongoing (or long-term) support. Some groups may bond so strongly that they continue to meet even after a structured group has ended. Although that provides for a long-term need, it doesn't always develop from a structured/closed group if a strong bond is not developed.

This structured/closed format requires a highly skilled and committed facilitator willing to devote a great deal of time and energy to the group. This format also works extremely well if co-facilitators are used, one male and one female. In this format, a team approach is used, and it helps in modeling the male/female issues.

Pastoral Care / Clergy

Death is an experience that often puts us in touch with our own mortality. This, in turn, leads us to question larger issues: Is this all there is?; What is beyond death?; What is the true meaning of death/life?; and many others. Spiritual issues often arise from loss, especially loss from death.

When the death seems particularly unjust, the bereaved will often question the fairness of life and death, and therefore the justness of a higher power. Even individuals whose faith in their higher power is very strong will often question this belief in the face of what is perceived to be an unjust death.

Humans probably perceive no more unjust or unfair death than the death of an innocent child. And no child is more innocent than the unborn who have not experienced life beyond their own birth. (Some denominations question the innocence of the unborn, believing that we inherit the sins of our forefathers, but few would dispute that the unborn child is without fault of their own doing.) As a result, perinatal loss will bring up issues of spirituality, and belief systems will be questioned or even challenged.

The most haunting question grieving parents face is, "Why?" Trying to find an answer, they may turn to their particular belief system. But many times, their beliefs can offer them little, if any, explanation as to "why?" Also, because most of us have an idea that our belief system is fair, a grieving couple will go back and forth from "Why?" to "Why us?"

In their continuing effort to find an answer to the "why" question, bereaved parents will tend to focus on what they did to bring this loss about. They will most often conclude that they are good people who don't deserve this. This comes from a mindset that doing good in life is some sort of insurance policy against anything bad happening. This struggle will eventually elevate to questioning the fairness of their higher power.

Questioning the fairness or the wisdom of their higher power is usually done in anger. Anger is, of course, a key element in the grieving process, and it is very common for grieving parents to become angry at their higher power.

However, God being *God,* we're not supposed to question or be angry at God. For many parents, this anger at their higher power will be immediately followed by guilt. Guilt itself is a powerful emotion, and in this context can often become debilitating. The guilt they feel for questioning their God is now combined with the tremendous guilt they are already feeling over the death of their child.

They have been over and over every minute they remember of the pregnancy, and they wonder, "What if I/we had done _______?", or, "What if I/we hadn't done _______?". By dwelling on what they should, or should not, have done to prevent the outcome, tremendous guilt will be produced.

The combined guilt about themselves and the guilt they feel toward their higher power can grow to the point of depression.

As a result, one of the first spiritual needs of grieving parents is to know that it is understandable that they are angry with God. Since the supreme being understands all things, certainly God will understand their anger and will not condemn them for it.

Secondly, God, being omnipotent, is the only one that will be able to answer the "why" question for them. Since we, the living, are not able to know God's answer, we have no choice but to accept that, at least for now, there *isn't* an answer.

Another paramount need of grieving parents is that their baby will be taken care of in whatever afterlife is a part of their particular belief system. Often they will want to know that the baby will remain a baby until they enter their own afterlife, and that they will be able to care for their own child there. These questions are different in each individual belief system, but the answers need to be carefully explained to the grieving parents in order to allay their fears and anxieties.

Some beliefs differentiate between babies who are baptized and those who are not. If the baby was not baptized, parents may become anxious that they didn't do what they were supposed to do to take care of the spiritual needs of their child. (Remember also that this compounds another issue in that they might feel that if they had properly taken physical care of themselves or their child, the baby would be alive.)

As clergy, be aware of this issue and that this fear may exist. If you sense fear in the parents, ask them what it is that they are fearful of. This direct approach usually works best. Many times, parents will have a form of free-floating anxiety which they may not even be able to pinpoint, and you may need to suggest some possibilities to them.

The issue of baptism also brings up a previously raised point. For those belief systems which believe a child is conceived in sin and needs forgiveness, baptism can be endowed as a ritual cleansing of the soul. Parents who embrace this belief system and suffer a perinatal loss may question whether such a ritual exists for their child.

If, in their belief system, a ceremonious, posthumous baptism is possible, it might offer them a great deal of comfort. If it is not possible, they need to be assured that they did nothing wrong, and that the baby will not suffer for not having been baptized. Be prepared, however, for them to question why there is no ritual for this particular situation.

What bereaved parents don't need are answers to their questions that are evasive, placating, contrite, or designed to only make them feel better. They don't need them because, frankly, they don't work. A good example is, "God only gives you what you can handle." The grieving, angry parent might answer: "Does that mean that if I were a weaker person that my baby would still be alive?"; or, "Well, it's a mean spirited God that took away my baby just because I could handle it!", or even, "So it *is* my fault that my baby is dead!"

Another statement to avoid: "God is taking care of your baby now." Although this might comfort a few, a grieving parent doesn't want anyone else taking care of their baby, and may resent God for doing what they feel they should be allowed to do. This resentment towards God, often unspoken, produces more guilt and more psychological and spiritual conflict.

Clergy will often be asked to perform a memorial service or possibly a funeral. This is a very difficult function to perform for a variety of reasons, not the least of which is the unexplainability of the death. Therefore, don't try to explain it.

The fact that as clergy you're being asked to perform a service for someone you've never met is probably not all that unusual. However, in this situation, you cannot get others who knew the deceased to tell you about them. You may struggle with what to say about the deceased. Rather than attempt to characterize the baby, keep in mind the needs of the parents. They need to have their loss and their pain validated. They need to have everyone in attendance know that this was their child, and how much this baby meant to them. They need to know that their child was cared for and loved for the time the baby was here, and that their baby is not in pain.

Words of comfort are a large part of the clergy's job description. But keep in mind that your words of comfort do not have to do miracles and erase the pain. Erasing pain is not something to be aspired to anyway, in that at the moment the pain may be all the parents feel they have left to honor their baby.

As a result, choose your words well. Badly chosen words of comfort may backfire and distance the grieving parents from their faith at a time when they probably need it most.

Another large role for the clergy is simply to "be there" for the parents. Grieving parents need all the support they can get, and because many of their loss issues may be spiritual in nature, the support of God's representative becomes extremely important. Keep this in mind especially for those who have suffered an early term loss, or miscarriage. These parents are receiving little, if any, support from anyone. Just letting the parents know that you are available to them in their time of need will lend a great deal of comfort and will validate their loss. It will also reassure them that God is not abandoning them. This may be critical if they harbor anger or animosity towards God for the loss and as a result are already wrestling with guilt.

Also remember that this is a major loss for the parents as a couple, and as such, will put a great strain on a marriage. (Refer to the section on Male vs. Female Grief). Follow up periodically with the couple to gauge how they are doing. In this way, they'll know they are not forgotten, and the continuing contact will let them know the power of what they experienced.

The subject of miscarriage, in particular, may present a spiritual crisis, that if not handled with care, can cause them to turn away from their specific religion. Considering that many religions believe that life begins at conception, why, then, is the death of an eight-week-old fetus not treated with the same respect as the death of an eight-year-old child? To some couples, this question presents a dilemma regarding a double standard that for them borders on hypocrisy.

Countless couples are suffering perinatal losses, particularly miscarriages, silently and unaddressed, while fellow parishioners whose living child dies are showered with sympathy, ceremonies and rituals. It is, therefore, the responsibility of clergy as the representative of a church, to fully recognize the death of a fetus as the death of a child by supporting the parents in their grief. While doing this, help the couple understand that they may encounter many individuals who won't understand their sense of loss. And, emphasize that in addition to spirituality, rituals are also steeped in history and culture, that has, unfortunately, not always recognized the strength of grief a parent has after a perinatal loss.

Funeral Directors

It is a fact that some babies die before they experience their own birth, and that this occurs in every community. Eventually, you will be called upon to assist with a service for a pre-birth death. These deaths inherently have special needs. Be prepared.

For example, a tiny casket will be overwhelmed if placed on a full size pier, so make sure a suitable alternative is available. (I was recently told a horror story in which a baby's casket was displayed sitting on a chair.) Always remember that this service needs to be handled with the same dignity and respect given any other service that you would conduct.

The funeral director is coming into contact with grieving parents when they may still be in shock and denial. Often, only the father is present to make arrangements. The full reality of what has happened may not have yet hit. But, making arrangements for their child's funeral—when they should be taking the child home—may be what pushes them into facing that reality. Be aware of this.

Contact with people who have just experienced loss is a normal experience for a funeral director. The bereaved are usually tearful and in pain because they are getting in touch with the loss of a person who was a part of their life. They might talk about memories of the person who has died.

In making funeral arrangements, they might comment "________ would have liked that," or, "________ wouldn't have wanted a big fuss made over them." Their character and personality are known and their likes, dislikes, favorite music, and favorite flower may all be known.

With a perinatal loss, none of this information is known. In fact, *knowing* becomes a part of what is lost. As funeral arrangements are being made, the scope of the loss may begin to become clear. They may begin to realize that they will never know what their child's favorite flower was, or what they liked or disliked. They will struggle to talk of their child as someone they have known. The reality is that they *have* known their child, but not in a traditional manner.

Be careful that you don't fall into the trap of trying to ease their pain or in any way diminish the importance of what they have lost. Don't say or imply that somehow it's easier to never have known. Or even worse, don't tell them they have no need to make arrangements for such a loss, and that you will "handle everything for them."

I was once told a story of a couple who incurred a loss at 19 weeks (one week short of "qualifying" as a stillbirth) who wanted to have a memorial service for their baby. Their local funeral home director dismissed the idea and told them they could do something on their own, but not at the funeral home. This action invalidated their loss and created enough confusion for them to eventually find their way into my office. They were confused because they were willing to pay for the use of the chapel at the funeral home, and all other expenses. Their only possible conclusion for why their business was being turned away was that their loss wasn't valid.

Also, a typical dynamic can develop when, as is often the case, the funeral director is male, and the person primarily making the arrangements is male. A grieving father, in the midst of his pain and confusion, often will tend to follow the lead of the professional—in this case, the funeral director. In a possible attempt at male bonding, and perhaps even his own lack of comfort with the issue of perinatal loss, the funeral director may take a very male posture: one of protector of the parents (especially the mother). The funeral director thinks that by taking over making the arrangements, and making them as simply and inexpensively as possible, the parents will be enabled to get on with their lives as quickly as possible.

This thinking in place, the funeral director believes he is doing the parents a great favor. However, in doing so, the mother is often left out of the decision-making process, which means she doesn't give feedback as to her needs. If the ceremony is not what the mother needs, she may not be able to say goodbye to her child or to have closure—two very important needs that are the basis for funeral services. In addition to this causing marital strife at a time when the couple least need it, it may also not address the father's needs. An important point, therefore, is that whenever possible, consult with *both* parents before making final arrangements so as to insure the service meets their needs. On those occasions when the father is primarily responsible for making arrangements, the funeral director might respectfully suggest that things that have been discussed be talked over with the mother before a final decision is made.

Most people, as they make funeral arrangements, are also simultaneously in touch with the past they have lost with the passing of their loved one. As grieving parents make arrangements after a perinatal loss, they are in touch with the loss of the future, not the past. The past they have experienced with their child is so nebulous as to almost not even exist. During the pregnancy, the only focus was the end result of the baby being born. It is only now, understanding that the joy of the birth will not happen, that the true joy of the pregnancy is beginning to be understood.

One of the best thoughts to keep in mind when working with a couple who have experienced a perinatal loss, is to validate their pain, their dilemma, their confusion, and their loss. For example, they may say a variation of, "Maybe we shouldn't even be doing this, after all, she wasn't even born."

Validating the reality that they *are* in the right place will help them resolve their dilemma. Explain that funeral arrangements are made when the living lose an important person in their life to death. The importance of a child to a parent is beyond question. Just because the child died before they could experience their own birth does not negate that importance.

Validation, which is extremely important to the couple, is as simple as letting them know that they are where they need to be, they are doing what they need to be doing, and that by making arrangements for their child they are creating memories they will later cherish. Know that creating memories is especially important when they have so few memories to cherish.

Because mementos become extremely important to parents who have so few memories, offer to keep for them anything that had connection with their child (i.e., the blanket the baby was wrapped in from the hospital, copies of paperwork regarding the baby, etc.) To create memories, allow them a private viewing, or offer to take a picture of the baby for the parents to keep. The more memories and mementos they can have, the better they will feel because they will provide an object link between the parent and child as additional validation.

Particular mementos have some difficulties inherent in them that warrant being addressed. For example, a parent being allowed a private viewing of their child needs to be prepared by the funeral director as to the effects of embalming, autopsy, normal tissue deterioration, etc., so they won't be shocked when they do see their baby. And, while a picture can provide great solace, it can be even more effective if taken correctly. Using warm (usually not fluorescent) lighting, wrapping the baby in earth toned cloth, holding the baby, all are ways to make the photograph less clinical.

For a variety of reasons, the option of cremation is often chosen rather than burial. This option allows the parents to finally take their child home, should they have that desire. Part of the attractiveness of cremation is that the ashes themselves become a memento. Cremation is also attractive to younger couples who may not be permanent residents where the baby died. They may be very reluctant to leave their child somewhere they will not be able to visit when they have the need to. Whatever their reason, it should be made clear to the parents that a decision for cremation does not eliminate the need for a service unless that is what they want.

Once arrangements have been made and the service is at hand, the scenario for the funeral director will probably be quite typical. It is important to keep a professional demeanor and not treat the situation any differently than you would any other service. Some of the guests might be struggling with the appropriateness and justification for the service. If any of the funeral staff are casual in their demeanor, this may validate their viewpoint that the service is, indeed, unnecessary and unjustified. Unfortunately, an individual feeling this way may feel free to share this opinion with the grieving couple, thereby causing obvious undue pain and/or conflict.

At the conclusion of the service, give the couple whatever mementos they have requested, give them assistance in gathering any flowers, cards or gifts that may have been delivered, and allow them whatever time they need to say their private goodbye to their baby.

A funeral, graveside service or memorial service of any kind can be a cherished memory for parents who have so few memories to cherish in the coming months and years. By assisting the grieving couple, the funeral director provides a dignified venue for the living to pay their last respects to the dead. Additionally, under the circumstance of a perinatal loss, the funeral director, by handling this situation with the same dignity given to any other death, gives validation and affirmation to individuals who may desperately need it.

Remember to listen to the parents, hear what it is they need, and guide them. Don't just do it for them. Remember that for them the events of the last few days have been a blur, and they are feeling pretty beaten and helpless. To take matters into your own hands may seem merciful, but you can later be perceived as another person who took advantage of them by doing what you wanted to do, at a time when they were particularly vulnerable. Hear what they need and proceed accordingly, and you'll be perceived as someone to be trusted. A positive experience will leave them feeling a little less helpless.

Clerical Staff

After a perinatal loss has occurred, there are many formalities that need to be taken care of. It is likely, therefore, that clerical staff will have contact with parents who are grieving. This contact needs to be handled with compassion and understanding.

Most of the grieving parents I've met are aware that forms have to filled out, records have to be kept, and that protocols have to be maintained. They are not opposed to being asked to "sign this," "fill out that," or whatever tasks are necessary. But at the same time, they are particularly sensitive to emotions—both their own and others—and to how they are being treated by those around them.

One mother told me a horror story about laying on an examination table in the emergency room, sobbing, after being told she had lost her baby. Suddenly, a clerk entered the examination room voicing her frustration because she didn't know the correct code for the patient's "condition." The mother's demeanor instantly changed from being in pain and tearful, to being angry.

She shrieked at the clerk, "My child is *dead!* How *dare* you make it just a *condition*!" This was a needlessly disastrous situation. The clerk ran out of the room in shock, the mother now felt angry, guilty, depressed and confused. This example clearly illustrates the need to have clerical staff trained not only to proper coding procedures, but to the issues faced by a grieving parent.

In this example, the clerk walked right into the major issue of perinatal loss: invalidation. The clerk, who was by the nature of her job trying to reduce the death of a child to a condition with a number attached, made her frustration with the situation more important than what the mother was dealing with. Had she been properly trained, she would have been aware of the seriousness of the loss, offered her condolences, compassionately asked the patient to sign the needed forms, all while keeping her coding problem to herself until she could get proper assistance from a supervisor.

This example illustrates how important it is that anyone with contact with a grieving parent, needs to be cognizant of what it is the parent(s) are going through. Although they obviously need to be aware of their job (completing paperwork, for example), they must do so with an empathy for the patient.

A clerical person in the hospital setting needs to be aware that a parent who has just been informed that her child has died is often in shock and is numb to what has just happened. What they need is validation of the magnitude of their loss, not someone who has only their own priorities in mind. Clerical staff who don't have the patient's emotional circumstances in mind will be met with resistance and anger, not cooperation. Even though the mother may be in shock, and may just go through the motions of cooperation, you can be assured that later she will remember who was validating and who was not.

The clerical person in the obstetrician's office faces the grieving mother at a different time. For example, an expectant mother may be given the news of her loss at the doctor's office. Despite the fact that clerical personnel will usually only have contact with the patient for a few brief seconds after the loss is explained, they need to be no less concerned or understanding of what the mother has just experienced. It can take just a few seconds to be remembered as validating, or invalidating, a parent's loss.

Scheduling appointments also requires contact between patient and clerk. At all costs, under all circumstances, avoid inappropriate comments. This insensitivity is not limited to the period of time *after* a loss. One grieving mother in my support group related a story of an appointment clerk at her obstetrician's office who cheerfully said to her, "See you next week, unless you have a miscarriage." The mother was only irritated at the comment until three days later when she actually did miscarry her baby. Then she became outraged at the comment.

However, most doctor's office personnel contact with grieving mothers will be during follow-up appointments. These contacts need to handled with compassion and concern for the mother's over-all well-being. Be aware that she is confused and hurting. She has just lost her future, and the significance of that may just be setting in.

If the loss occurred later in the pregnancy, the mother may still appear pregnant. Don't make the grievous mistake of treating her that way. This means you will need to know what is going on with the patients, so make sure you stay informed.

As she signs in for a follow-up appointment, don't be as cheerful and bubbly as you would for an expectant mother. This mother's needs are different and she needs special consideration. A simple, "Hi, it's good to see you," will do. If you are prepared for the answer, it is appropriate to ask, "How are you doing?" But ask that question only if you are willing to deal with the true answer. If you have the need to say something addressing the loss, good examples might be: "You've been in my thoughts a lot..." or "I want you to know how you're loss has touched my life..." or "I know it's hard being here again after your loss...."

Remember, patients are not just names on a chart, so don't

treat them as though they are. It will be helpful to be sensitive to the patient's demeanor. If, for example, you notice that she is anxious and uncomfortable, and you look around the waiting room and it's full of bulging expectant mothers, try to arrange a room for her to wait in other than the waiting room.

Always look at the appointment list so you'll know if someone who has incurred a loss is coming in. Then you won't be caught off guard and not know what to do. If you notice the patient having a difficult time holding herself together, let one of the nursing staff know what you've observed. They may be better equipped to do something for her. At the very least, they will want to be aware of what you observed so that they are not caught off guard when they, and the doctor, do see her.

Most of all, validate the patient's loss. Don't say or do anything that minimizes what she is experiencing. Don't try to give her your answers, or say something just to make her feel better. Be professional in your role, keep your issues to yourself, and handle her with the same kind of care and compassion you would want in a similar circumstance.

Genetic Counselors

Genetic counseling is a relatively new field. Only in recently medical history have we come to realize how much information is passed on genetically from parent to child, and therefore from generation to generation.

Parents who have suffered a perinatal loss often wonder if their loss was genetic in origin and will often seek out the advice of a genetic counselor to answer their questions. Unfortunately, many times grieving parents are looking to a genetic counselor to answer questions that either don't have answers, or, at the very least, don't have genetic answers.

As we've previously discussed, grieving parents are often struggling with the "Why?" question. Of course, this the the main question that the parents hope the genetic counselor will be able to answer. Unfortunately, even if the counselor can answer the genetic/medical "Why?" questions, the parents will soon find they are still left with "Why me/us?" Therefore, it is advisable that the role of the genetic counselor be very carefully explained and session(s) be very structured for the grieving parents so they don't look to the counselor to provide more than they are capable of.

Grieving parents will also look for concrete concepts to hang on to, when so much of what they are experiencing is abstract. They have the tendency to look for concrete (black/white) explanations. What they will more than likely get, however, are statistics and probabilities. Keep in mind that while statistics and probabilities definitely have value, it often is not what the parents want to hear. In fact, grieving parents may view statistics and probabilities as as an attempt at an evasive answer that is designed to absolve guilt or blame.

The best way to disarm this possibility is to simply address the issue and provide as much explanation as possible. Start by explaining that medicine, contrary to popular belief, is not an exact science. The practice of medicine is just that: practice. No one is its master (this being one of the many reasons people pursue careers in the field—you'll never master it, you'll always be learning). Medicine is highly educated (and practiced) judgement based upon empirical evidence and probabilities of outcomes. At the same time, come right out and say, "I know that statistics and probabilities may sound evasive, but they are the only way we have of truly coming to full understanding of what happened and how it relates to what may happen." You need to help the couple see the "big picture" rather than their understandably very focused (due to their pain) point of view. Remember, however, that you may have to address this issue more than once for the parents to truly "hear" it.

The vast majority of couples I have worked with want straight answers to their questions, not just something that will make them feel better. They are confronted almost constantly with people who are trying to make them feel better by fixing their pain. From health care professionals, they need honesty. Most of the couples want to know what caused the death of their baby. This includes knowing if there is a genetic problem that one or both of the parents may possess. Although this is difficult news to hear, most parents will want to know the truth, as opposed to not knowing at all.

If a genetic problem is discovered with either one or both parents, be aware that this may feed into guilt that may already be present. Be prepared to disarm the power that the guilt wields by simply making the parent aware they couldn't do anything about what they didn't know. They made the only decision they could under the circumstances. This approach will not eliminate the guilt but will lessen its power. This is as much as you can hope to do.

Once the parents know that there is a genetic problem, they will want to know if there is anything that can be done about it. They will want to know if the situation can be controlled. Since their loss has affected the feeling of having control over their lives, they quite naturally want to know what they can do to control the next pregnancy.

However, as every genetic counselor knows, having the knowledge of a specific genetic problem doesn't always provide control. As one genetic counselor told me, "Often, I'm telling patients what *could* or *could not* happen, not what *will* or *will not* happen." Sometimes the truth will even heighten the sense of the loss of control which the parents are already feeling. Keep this in mind as you answer the couple's questions.

On the other hand, you may inform the parents that there is not a genetic problem, and that the loss was probably an aberration. If this is the case, the parents are often told this news by their physician, but they may wish to verify it by also speaking to the genetic counselor. If the loss was not genetically oriented, and was a more random occurrence, this, too, may heighten the parents' feelings of lost control. Either way, be prepared to address the control issue with them, as it surely will arise.

Hospital Social Workers

The social worker holds a diverse role in the hospital setting. They are responsible for meeting the psychological/emotional needs of the patients they see, and activating social systems within and outside of the hospital in order to meet those needs. Unfortunately, the social worker usually has an extremely limited time in which to accomplish their task. Under normal circumstances, a patient experiencing a perinatal loss spends a very limited amount of time, if any, in the hospital. Especially in miscarriages, the patient is in and out of the Emergency Room before the social work staff is even notified. In the case of later-term losses, at least an overnight stay will be involved.

Therefore, social worker contact with the parents will be of short duration, usually limited to the beginning when the loss is still a new experience. The patient and partner will both be in shock over what has just happened. They may operate like zombies—just going through the motions and doing what they are told to do. They may be tearful, but the full depth of the emotional pain hasn't yet hit them because a full understanding of what they have actually lost still has not hit them.

The social worker will mainly need to prepare them for what to expect when they leave the hospital. They need to be not only a listening ear, but also a guide as to what the immediate future will hold for them.

Discuss the grieving process and the various stages they will move through. Help them become familiar enough with grief that they know they are not losing their minds or just going crazy. Validate the numbness they are currently experiencing. Make sure to at least briefly cover the differences in male vs. female grieving styles. In the midst of their pain they may be grieving the same, but very soon they will begin to sound and act very differently. By discussing the differences, you may at least prepare them for that eventuality.

Don't let them leave the hospital with false expectations. Be realistic with them. They may want to know how long it will be before they "get over it." This implies that they want a time when they will forget. But, this is not something they will "get over." Explain to them that forgetting may be attractive now, but there will be a time when they really won't want to forget and assure them they never will.

One of the ways they won't forget is to make sure they have as many mementos of their baby as possible. One of the roles a social worker can play is to gather all the things that could be used as baby mementos. Anything that came into contact with, or had anything to do with, the baby will fulfill this need.

If the mother and baby were in several different locations within the hospital, mementos can be lost. The social worker is in a good position to act as a coordinator and gatherer of these items for the parents. If someone goes through this effort, the grieving couple may recognize the importance of these items, and will appreciate the attention that has been given to these details. Again, this provides a great deal of validation at a time when the parents are in need of all they can get.

At the same time, let them know that others may not always be as sympathetic or understanding of their pain. Assure them that they don't have to take on what others tell them, and that it is OK for them to experience their pain.

Another service that the social worker can provide for the couple is to assess the adequacy of the support system they have around them. If the support system is inadequate for their needs, one should be established for them.

Hospital staff may be in contact with those people in the couple's life who are important to them: grandparents, parents, brothers, sisters, close friends, pastor, etc. By coaching these people in some of the issues of perinatal loss and what the couples needs, they can become advocates for the grieving couple. This not only creates a support system for the grieving couple, but can help insure that the people around them will not impose so many of their own issues regarding perinatal loss on the parents. The main goal of the social worker is to insure that the support system works for the grieving couple, and not against them.

If it becomes obvious that the support system does not exist or that it is dysfunctional and destructive, then the social worker needs to help the couple provide for their own needs. Coach them on how to not take on others' advice if it just doesn't feel right for them. Let them know that it's OK to seek out people who will be supportive in the ways they need. Give them permission to take care of themselves in whatever form that may take. Additionally, let them know your willingness (within the scope of your job, your skills, and your available time) to take whatever active advocate role would be deemed appropriate.

If this type of involvement is felt to be inappropriate at your hospital (as it is at some), then let the couple know of outside resources available to them. If there are support groups in your area, make sure the couple is aware of them and encourage them to attend. If there are therapists who specialize in grief issues (especially the loss of a child), provide those names. If you know of books on the subject that others have found helpful, share that knowledge with them.

If these resources are not available in your area, decide in what fashion you can create them. If there is no support group currently in your area, consider starting one (discussion of support groups is in the section on Therapists/Counselors). Keep a bibliography of helpful books on the subjects related to perinatal loss.

As you hear back from couples who have had losses and have healed, ask if they would be willing to talk to couples who are in the midst of their pain. Keep a list of their telephone numbers along with a description of their loss. This way, you can refer a patient to a couple who has experienced a similar loss. Matching couples who have similar losses will help them more rapidly develop a personal bond.

Make sure there is some form of follow-through with the couple. Speak to both the father and the mother to find out how they are doing, what they are feeling, what they are doing. Speaking to both parents is important because husbands, in their need to "protect" their wives, will often report their wife as doing "fine" when the reality may be far from that. A follow up contact becomes essential when a mother incurs an early term loss, and is in and out of the ER before a social worker is informed.

A simple phone contact can become a powerful tool on several levels. For example: "Hello, I'm ______, a Social Worker at ______ Hospital. I understand that on ______ you were admitted to our Emergency Room with a diagnosis of miscarriage. First of all, we recognize what a powerful loss you have incurred, and wanted to voice the condolences of all of us here at ______ Hospital. I also wanted to personally check and see how you're doing."

In a simple phone call, caring, compassion, validation of the loss, and a concern for the medical well-being of the patient are all being communicated. It is also an opportunity to share some of the previously mentioned information (books, support groups, etc.) with a patient that you were not able to meet with at the hospital.

Often, the follow-up call can gain information on the medical condition of the mother. But also, by extending the conversation a little, other vital information can be gathered. Has there been any adverse affect regarding eating/sleeping habits, depression, suicidal thoughts, psychotic episodes, etc.? It is at this point of follow-through that an evaluation/assessment can be crucial. If there are emotional or psychological concerns, a referral can be made early.

At the very least, a follow-up phone call will let the patient know that they are cared about, and that what they went through was a truly powerful experience. And, for those perhaps rare occasions when psychosis is assessed, another personal disaster for the grieving parents can hopefully be averted.

Caregiver Renewal

As caregivers, we give of ourselves—our talents, our experience, and our expertise—to those in need. We do this as a profession, as a career, and sometimes as a "calling." For most of us, we have undertaken this role of professional caregiver in order to fulfill certain character traits that destined us for this work. However, those same character traits which drive us to do what we do (and do well), can also drive us to *over* do. We will invariably take care of others before, and sometimes to the exclusion of, ourselves.

Many of us grew up programmed to believe that selfishness was evil. Well, I think selfishness has gotten a bad rap. Selfishness, in and of itself, is not a bad thing. Like many similar concepts, selfishness taken to extremes indeed does become something deplorable— it becomes self-centeredness. But, this speaks more to being ego-centric and narcissistic rather than selfish.

Caregiving, at least on the surface, seems to be the antithesis of selfishness. And yet, caregiving taken to extremes also becomes deplorable and just as dysfunctional. Caregiving taken to extremes becomes co-dependency and enmeshment. When this happens, we become weaker and have less and less to give to the people who are in need because we, ourselves, have become needy.

Selfishness is, in actuality, taking care of ourselves. As a caregiver, this means taking care of ourselves in order to have a greater capacity to give from ourselves the caring that others need. It must be within before it can be given to others. We must replenish ourselves in whatever individual ways work for us.

There are several things to consider about replenishment. First of all, *know your limitations.* We all have them. Accept that they are a part of life. For example, as an eleven gallon blood donor, I know not to give blood when I'm feeling run down, tired, have a cold, etc. If I did give blood under these conditions, not only do I endanger myself, but also all those who will receive any part of the unit of blood I have donated. In other words, I haven't done *anyone* any favors. The key is to know yourself well enough to know when you need to *not* be giving of yourself.

Do your own work. If you have grieving to do, or issues in your own life to face, deal with them before dealing with other people's issues. For example, I was first asked to facilitate the support group that I currently run when my wife was pregnant for the second time. I turned down the offer for two reasons. First, the stillbirth of my daughter had only occurred five months previous, and I didn't feel I was ready. And secondly, we were extremely invested in the second pregnancy and understandably very anxious about its outcome. I knew I wouldn't have been much use to anyone attending a perinatal loss support group. I wasn't finished doing my own work yet. After our healthy son was born, the offer was made again, and I accepted because I then felt I was ready. I hope my example illustrates the point: when we give care to others before we have fully dealt with the same issue present in our own life, we do both of us an injustice.

Learn to receive as well as you give. If there is only value in what others receive from you, what does that say? Having the courage to let others know that we are not omnipotent is to allow them to see us as human. And never forget that is what we all are—human—and that we're all in this together. Once we accept this, we can also begin to trust that others can survive without us.

Learn to set boundaries. Often we have such a difficult time saying "no." It's much easier to draw a line and say, "Up to this line, I'm gladly willing to do all that I can. Past this line, I'm not." In this way we communicate our willingness to help others, but we also model our willingness to equally take care of ourselves. This is important. Remember that if we do our job well, our care becomes obsolete to our patients, and they'll know they can take care of themselves because they can see us doing it.

We all find renewal in our own way. For some it takes the form of wandering shopping malls, flea markets or garage sales in search of bargains. For others, it is intense athletic activities, playing the piano, sailing, watching movies, or reading a novel. The list is almost infinite.

To use myself once again as an example: years ago I purchased a Jeep CJ7 as a "toy" (we all know that men need their toys). Today it has become my mental health vehicle. Often I'll take a Friday off from work, climb into my Jeep, and hit the road. Sometimes I'll go by myself, other times with a friend. Sometimes I go to the beach, sometimes to the nearby national forest, and sometimes I simply drive or run errands I've been putting off. Whatever I do, the openness of my vehicle, the wind in my face and the sun on my head provide me with a sense of freedom and perspective. It truly works for me. But whatever your vehicle to mental health might be, *using* it is what epitomizes the philosophy of self-responsibility that often we try to instill in patients and need to practice ourselves. Taking care of yourself truly allows you to, as the personalized tag on my Jeep reads: B WHO UR.

Bibliography

Allen, Marie & Marks, Shelly, *Miscarriage: Women Sharing from the Heart.* New York, NY: John Wiley & Sons, 1993.

American Psychiatric Association, *Diagnostic & Statistical Manual of Mental Disorders* (Third Edition-Revised). Washington, D.C., 1987.

American Psychiatric Association, *Diagnostic & Statistical Manual of Mental Disorders* (Fourth Edition). Washington, D.C., 1994.

Borg, Susan, & Lasker, Judith, *When Pregnancy Fails; Families Coping with Miscarriage, Stillbirth and Infant Death*. New York, NY: Bantam Books, 1989.

Davis, Deborah L., *Empty Cradle, Broken Heart: Surviving the Death of Your Baby*. Golden, CO: Fulcrum Publishing, 1991.

Davies, Phyllis, *Grief: Climb Towards Understanding*. New York, NY: Carol Communications, 1988.

Defrain, John D., *Stillborn: The Invisible Death*. Lexington, MA: Heath Lexington Books, 1986.

Doka, Kenneth L., *Disenfranchised Grief.* New York, NY: Lexington Books, 1989.

Ewy, Donna & Roger, *Death of a Dream: Miscarriage, Stillbirth, Infant Death*. EP Dutton, Inc., 1984.

Friedman, Rochelle, & Gradstein, Bonnie, *Surviving Pregnancy Loss*. Boston, MA: Little, Brown & Company, 1982.

Gilbert, Kathleen R. and Smart, Laura S., *Coping with Infant or Fetal Loss: The Couple's Healing Process*. New York, NY: Brunner/Mazel Publications, 1992.

Goldman, Linda, *Life & Loss: A Guide To Help Grieving Children.* Muncie, IN: Accelerated Development, Inc., 1994.

Gryte, Marilyn, *When A Baby Dies*. Tucson, AZ: Carondelet, 1994.

Gryte, Marilyn, *No New Baby*. Omaha, NE: Centering Corporation, 1988.

Hayford, Jack, *I'll Hold You in Heaven*. Ventura, CA: Regal Books, 1986.

Hughes, Marylou, *Bereavement and Support: Healing in a Group Environment*. Bristol, PA: Taylor & Francis, 1995.

Ilse, Sherokee, *Empty Arms: Coping with Miscarriage, Stillbirth, and Neonatal Death*. Long Lake, MN: Wintergreen Press, 1982.

Ilse, Sherokee, & Burns, Linda, *Miscarriage: A Shattered Dream.* Long Lake, MN: Wintergreen Press, 1985.

James, John W., & Cherry, Frank, *The Grief Recovery Handbook.* New York, NY: Harper & Row, 1988.

Johnson, Joy and Johnson, Marvin, *A Most Important Picture - a very tender manual for taking pictures of stillborn babies and infants who die.* Omaha, NE: Centering Corp., 1985.

Lamb, Sister Jane Marie, *Bittersweet: Hello/Goodbye. A resource in planning farewell rituals when a baby dies.* St. Charles, MO: National Share Office, 1988.

Kaushner, Harold S., *When Bad Things Happen To Good People.* New York, NY: Avon Books, 1981.

Kohn, Ingrid, & Moffitt, Perry-Lynn, *A Silent Sorrow: Pregnancy Loss Guidance and Support for You and Your Family.* New York, NY: Bantam Books, 1993.

Luebbermann, Mimi, *Coping with Miscarriage: A Simple, Reassuring Guide to Emotional and Physical Healing.* Rocklin, CA: Prima Publishing, 1995.

Rando, Therese A., *Grief, Dying and Death: Clinical Interventions for Caregivers.* Omaha, NE: Centering Corp.

Rando, Therese A., *Parental Loss of a Child.* Champagne, IL: Research Press Co., 1986.

Rando, Therese A., *Treatment of Complicated Mourning.* Champagne, IL: Research Press Co., 1993.

Rank, Maureen, *Free to Grieve.* Minneapolis, MN: Bethany House, 1985.

Rich, Laurie A., *When Pregnancy Isn't Perfect.* New York, NY: Plume, 1991.

Rosof, Barbara, *The Worst Loss: How Families Heal from the Death of a Child.* New York, NY: Henry Holt & Co., 1994.

Scher, Jonathon and Dix, Carol, *Preventing Miscarriage - The Good News.* New York, NY: Harper & Row Publishers, 1990.

Schwiebert, Pat, & Kirk, Paul, *Still to be Born: A Guide for Bereaved Parents Who are Making Decisions About Their Future.* Portland, OR: Perinatal Loss, 1989.

Schwiebert, Pat & Kirk, Paul, *When Hello Means Goodbye.* Portland, OR: Perinatal Loss, 1985.

Shapiro, Constance Hoenk, *Infertility and Pregnancy Loss.* San Francisco, CA: Jossey-Bass Inc., 1988.

Staudacher, Carol, *Beyond Grief: A Guide for Recovering from the Death of a Loved One.* Oakland, CA: New Harbinger Publications, 1987.

Staudacher, Carol, *Men & Grief.* Oakland, CA: New Harbinger Publications, 1991.

Toder, Francine, *When Your Child Is Gone: Learning to Live Again.* New York, NY: Fawcett Crest, 1986.

Vineyard, Sue, *How To Take Care Of You...So You Can Take Care Of Others.* Downs Grove, IL: Heritage Arts Publishing.

Webb, Nancy Boyd, *Helping Bereaved Children: A Handbook for Practitioners.* New York, NY: Guilford Press, 1993.

Woods, James and Esposito, Jennifer, *Pregnancy Loss: Medical Therapeutics and Practical Considerations.* Baltimore, MD: Williams & Wilkins, 1987.

Worden, William J., *Grief Counseling & Grief Therapy.* New York, NY: Springer Publishing Co., Inc., 1991.

Resources / Information

A PLACE TO REMEMBER, 1885 University Avenue, Suite 110, Saint Paul, MN 55104, toll-free (800) 631-0973. *Sells birth/death and comfort/sympathy cards, baby memory box and memory book, books on the topic of perinatal loss, and other support materials.*

ALLIANCE OF GENETIC SUPPORT GROUPS, 33 Wisconsin Circle, #440, Chevy Chase, MD 20815, 1-800-336-GENE or (301) 652-5553. *Provides educational materials and referrals to consumers regarding most birth defects and genetic disorders. Referrals to parents, genetics professionals, support groups and organizations.*

AMEND, 4324 Berrywick Terrace, St. Louis, MO 63128.

CENTERING CORPORATION, 1531 N. Saddle Creek Rd., Omaha, NE 68104-5064, (402) 553-1200. *Sells literature on death, dying, and coping with bereavement issues, including divorce, illness, disability, death of children, adults and pets.*

CENTER FOR LOSS IN MULTIPLE BIRTH, INC. (CLIMB), c/o Jean Kollantai, PO Box 1064, Palmer, AK 99645, (907) 746-6123. An organization by and for parents who have experienced the death of one or more, both or all of their children during a multiple pregnancy, at or after birth, or in childhood. Has quarterly newsletter, parent contact list for support and other information.

HEAL, C/O Gary E. Vogel, M.A., Center for Women's Medicine, 2520 North Orange Ave, Orlando, Florida 32804, (407) 897-1617.

INTENSIVE CARE UNLIMITED, 910 Bent Lane, Philadelphia, PA 19118, (215) 233-4723. A bi-monthly non-profit newsletter to share info and resources for those who care for children who are premature, high-risk or have special problems. Also for those experiencing high-risk pregnancy or those who have lost a child.

PARENT CARE, INC., 9041 Colgate St., Indianapolis, IN 46268-1210, (317) 872-9913. A national source of information, direct referrals and forums for discussion, services to families, parent support groups, professionals concerned with infants who require intensive or special care at birth. Newsletter, literature, referrals to groups and annual national conference.

PEN PARENTS, Inc., PO Box 8738, Reno, NV 89507-8738, (702) 826-7332, FAX (702) 826-7332. A correspondence network for parents who have suffered the tragedy of pregnancy loss or the death of a child. Two newsletters: the one for pregnancy interruption is "A Heartbreaking Choice." Also a good resource for professionals.

PERINATAL LOSS, 2116 NE 18th Avenue, Portland, OR 97212, (503) 284-7426. *Booklets, cards and videos available for purchase.*

PREGNANCY & INFANT LOSS CENTER, 1415 E. Wayzata Blvd, Suite 22, Wayzata, MN 55391, (612) 473-9372. *A national non-profit that offers local and national support group information, a parent-to-parent peer support program, and literature for sale.*

RTS BEREAVEMENT SERVICES, Lutheran Hospital - LaCrosse, 1910 South Ave, Lacrosse, WI 54601, 1-800-362-8567, ext. 4747. *Hospital-based organization offering a support group, literature, and professional education after miscarriage, stillbirth, and neonatal death.*

SHARE, c/o Sr. Lane Marie Lamb, St. Elizabeth's Hospital, 211 South Rd, Belleville, IL 62222, (314) 947-6164. *Offers support to families who have had a miscarriage, stillbirth or infant death. Provides a newsletter, network of worldwide support groups, literature and referrals.*

TAPESTRY BOOKS, PO Box 359, Ringoes, NJ 08551-0359. Offers an extensive catalog of a couple of hundred resources specifically for adoption and infertility. World Wide Web site address is http://www.webcom.com/~tapestry.